Richard Smyth

An Indifference of Birds

Uniformbooks 2020

First published 2020
Copyright © Richard Smyth
Extract from 'Dead Reckoning' courtesy Richard Georges
ISBN 978-1-910010-22-8

Uniformbooks
7 Hillhead Terrace, Axminster, Devon EX13 5JL
uniformbooks.co.uk

Trade distribution in the UK by Central Books
centralbooks.com

Printed and bound by T J International, Padstow, Cornwall

For Genevieve

They say birds always find their way back home
but home is a nowhere—a memory; a never was.

Do wings remember spaces in the air
the way we might a place?...

Richard Georges, 'Dead Reckoning'

Prologue

Think of it as a murmuration.

Picture a cloud of starlings making Möbius shapes against a petrol-blue sky as the landscape beneath—a reedbed, a market town, the ruin of a pier, a stand of sycamores—is subsumed by dusk. The cloud furls and unfurls, puckers, pleats, is stretched and scrunched, inverting, infolding, impossibly elastic. The only constant here is change. The only thing you can predict is that in a half-second's time it won't look the same as it did a half-second ago.

Now imagine it's not five or ten thousand birds but many more than that. More than the multiple-million flocks of red-billed quelea whose wingbeats roar like breaking waves over the plains of sub-Saharan Africa. More than the boom-time mass-migrations of passenger pigeons that were said to darken the skies of the US in the nineteenth century.

Imagine billions of birds. Pan out and imagine the shifting shapes made by every bird on earth, a vast swirl of jabbering biomass, amorphous as magnetic flux or the currents of the oceans. Now run it at x1000 speed, and watch: watch as the shapes warp and dwindle, divide and subdivide; watch as the swarming cloud-particles—each a sparrow, or a gull, or a parakeet, or a thrush, or a falcon, or an auk, or a swallow, or a motmot, or an eagle, or a dove—come together and fall apart.

The only constant here is change. This is the world in which we live; this is the world we share with the birds.

There are other patterns, of course. The history of life on earth is the history of the interplay of these patterns. Slow ripples of geological motion, tides of climate change, flows and contraflows of other orders and genera, insects, reptiles, fish, microbes, mammals—and us. Roll back the film perhaps two, three million years, and pause: *there* we are, the hominids, the first humans, fanning out of east Africa, straightening up, looking out. And the birds are there, too. Watching. The birds were always there.

Birds were old when we were young. The first birds were theropods, hollow-boned dinosaurs, skinny, plumed and meat-eating, leaping in half-flight through the gingko forests of the mid Jurassic, one hundred and sixty-odd million years ago. The biggest mammals back then could curl up comfortably in a stegosaur footprint.

Where today, in the corrugated high forests of Liaoning province, north-east China, Pacific swifts zip through the upper air and the strangled rasps of black-naped orioles sound in the canopy, *Anchiornis huxleyi*, jackdaw-sized, blunt-snouted, feather-legged, would have hunted, fought, mated, reared young, and died, long before the Himalayas rose from the flatlands to the south. Where today beetle-black grackles crowd the powerlines of the Dallas-Fort Worth metroplex, *Austinornis lentus*—a first pheasant or junglefowl—pecked and scraped a living in the steamy maritime climate of ancient Texas. And back when 'Europe' was a marshy archipelago, knee-deep in the turbid waters of the Sea of Tethys, what's now the limestone lakeland of south-east Germany was the fenland home of *Archaeopteryx*, the *Ürvogel*, the 'first bird'—*Archaeo-pteryx*, the ancient feather.

The upright ape *Sahelanthropus* was aeons in the future. Waddling *Australopithecus*, heavy-jawed *Paranthropus*, *Homo habilis*, the 'handy man', wide-roaming *Homo heidelbergensis*, our enigmatic close cousin *Homo neanderthalensis*: all of these, every variety of human primate, were separated from the first birds by an unimaginable leap in time. From a human point of view, birds have always been here. No human was ever born into a birdless world. Picture again that great murmuration of all the birds of earth, milling in their many trillions across the shifting continents, across a hundred millennia. Our history, human history, is a late intrusion, a last-minute spanner in the birds' workings.

We remain small in the scale of ornithological time but from where we stand we can see that, where we go, where we do our human things, the pattern buckles. Things change—and while, of course, things have always changed, and always will change, these changes, the warpings and vanishings in our human airspace, they're *ours*. They're not just drift. They're consequences.

Where we act, the birds respond. Birds have never been a lumpen resource for us to plunder. They're not a mineral seam or an oilfield. The world of birds is a dynamic thing: it watches and reacts to everything we do. We and the birds are knotted in an unfathomable symbiosis.

From within the confines of a human lifetime, we really only ever see a snapshot of all this, the world lit by a momentary flashbulb burst. It can seem, sometimes, that everything is still. There have always been blackbirds in the yard. There have always been kittiwakes on the cliffs. There have always been swallows in springtime.

"When I see our ravens I have a feeling, almost, that this island is not mine, but theirs", wrote the naturalist R. M. Lockley in 1939, from his remote home on the Pembrokeshire island of Skokholm. "They have been here from time immemorial. They are, so to speak, indestructible, for they are believed to pair for life, and when one of the pair dies, a young bird immediately steps in to fill the gap. The ravens have been there though all the gaps in the occupation of the island by man, and will probably continue long after man has finished with Skokholm."

Time immemorial: time that we can't remember. But human memories are short. Perhaps the Skokholm rabbit farmers of the fourteenth century did hear the *gronk* of the raven from the mudstone cliffs. Perhaps the raven did cast its shadow, thick-bodied, long-fingered, over the settlements of Iron Age islanders. We don't know. *Can* we know?

There are ravens' nests on the crystalline rockfaces of western Greenland. There, too, at the stony edges of the icefield, are other nests—ancient nests. Littered with harebones, caked in centuries' worth of excrement, the nests of Greenland's gyrfalcons are among the oldest bird settlements ever found. By sampling the thick and long-accreting layers of falcon guano, scientists have dated the origins of some nests here to perhaps 2,700 years ago. This means that gyrfalcons have nested on these sites, these exact sites, for just about as long as a city called Rome has stood on the seven hills. A gyrfalcon, pale, dark-speckled and heavy-shouldered, glaring peregrine-like out at the slate-grey Atlantic, settled herself here to lay two or three eggs of tarnished gold at about the same time as Assyria was laying siege to Tyre, and Hoshea, his kingdom's last king, came to the throne of Israel. They were there then, and they are there now: hunting hare and ptarmigan, and crying *kya, kya, kya* from the cold cliffsides.

But 700 BCE is really not so long ago. Even the six-thousand-year occupancy of a penguin colony on Adelaide Island, Antarctica—evidenced by a metres-deep penguin midden of guano, nest-stones, eggshells and dead chicks—doesn't mean much, on the scale of bird-time, though it was founded before Thebes, before Hebron, before Athens. Change is still what birds are all about.

When I was born, in 1978, there were still cornfields on the English mainland where the ratcheting call of the corncrake could be regularly heard. There aren't now. There were no red kites in Britain, outside of a few wooded cwms in mid-Wales. Now they're everywhere: winnowing their tails in motorway updrafts, lurching into heavy flight from country-lane roadkill, squabbling with urban magpies for takeaway leftovers. There are parakeets stripping bare bird-feeders in London back gardens and cranes dancing in the Norfolk fenlands. The world is different; *we're* different, and so are the birds.

There's a famous and much-loved poem by Ted Hughes, about swifts. It tends to do the rounds on Twitter every June. *They've made it again*, it goes, *Which means the globe's still working*. It's a poem that looks at the world against a short scale. If the globe's really still working, there'll come a time when spring arrives without the swifts; there'll come a time, sooner or later, when the swifts go somewhere else, or stay where they are, in Congo or Rwanda, or perhaps when there simply aren't any swifts, here or anywhere. The world has been without swifts before.

History isn't so much about the passage of time as the study of change. How did we get from then to now, from there to here? To write the history of birds and people, you can look at how they've changed us—how their faces stare out in daubed red ochre from our cave-art, how their songs echo through the pages of our poetry, how we've dressed ourselves in their bones and feathers, taught ourselves to read the code of their microbi-ology—or you can look at how we've changed them. This book seeks to do the second thing. This is a book about our place in their history.

No nightingale ever wrote an ode about John Keats and no snowy heron or Carolina parakeet ever painted a portrait of John James Audubon, but we've shaped the history of birds—even the culture of birds—in a thousand other ways. Often without mean-ing to, we've disturbed the currents of their perpetual motion. We've drawn them to us and we've driven them away; our movements in the world, sometimes deft, sometimes fumbling, have kicked up opportunities, hazards, vectors of change, reasons for fear or flight.

Robert Burns saw a headlouse busy in the bonnet of a lady in church, and wrote of what a fine thing it would be had human-kind the power *to see oursels as others see us*. This book is about humanity, about us, as we must look to the birds; it's the story of human history, from a bird's eye view.

1. *Messy Eaters*

We're messy eaters. We always have been. When our ancestors moved in foraging bands through the rainforest they left feasts in their wake: broken honeycombs, fruit husks, pits and stones damp with pulp, crumbs of kola nut. This, perhaps, was why birds first noticed us—or not us at all (we were too big to be regarded, too heavy and slow, barely on the same plane of existence as a bird weighing a couple of ounces) but our footprint, the shadow we cast, the circles of consequences that spread out about us.

We are litterbugs of long standing, like most apes. From a bird's perspective it is one of our most appealing characteristics (up to a point, at least). When we began to hunt, we left behind us the bones and cartilage of our kills: vultures and carnivorous storks would have taken note. When, eventually, in the lull of post-glaciation some ten thousand years ago, we began to cultivate crops, we again showed ourselves to be usefully wasteful, helpfully careless—we'll talk more about that later. But we'd already become known, to the birds around us, for our leavings.

It wasn't just a question of what we left behind us; our impacts rippled out in all directions. Where we trampled the understorey, pulled down branches, prised the bark from treetrunks, where our heavy footsteps fell, small things fled from us. These got the birds' attention. Maybe this was our first identity, in the eyes of the birds watching on: to them, we were not tool-users, word-makers, builders, hunters, but just a mighty racket in the forest foliage—we were scarer-uppers, beaters for the birds' hunt.

We see it today. In the neotropics of Central America, doubletoothed kites—the sparrowhawks of the jungle—lurk on the fringes of troops of feeding tamarins and capuchins, ready to snatch the whirring cicadas that the monkeys flush from the canopy. Jacanas in the marshy forest clearings of the Congo basin profit from the clumsy intrusions of our cousins the gorillas. In south-east Brazil, olivaceous woodcreepers, insect-eating songbirds, mop up after golden lion tamarins. Yellow-casqued hornbills have dug even deeper into the local primate ecosystem: they've learned, feeding among Diana monkeys in west Africa, to read the monkeys' alarm calls, and to fear only the call that says 'crowned eagle', and not the call that says 'leopard' (eagles will hunt hornbills, leopards won't). Perhaps the forebears of these birds eavesdropped on our first indistinct Ardipithecene words, and made something of them, whatever they were.

Among ancient people and ancient birds, these interactions extended beyond the forests.

Hominoids, human-like primates, have roamed Namibia, in south-west Africa, since the mid-Miocene, around thirteen million years ago. We know *Otavipithecus namibiensis* only as a piece of ape's jawbone studded with a dozen broken teeth, dug from sedimentary rocks in the north of the country. It would, we think, have been a woodland animal: it would have had its own relationships with the far-back ancestors of the woodcreeper and kite. Not until perhaps two million years ago did we—that is, the great[100]-grandchildren of *Otavipithecus*—step out of the shadows of the trees. A site in south-west Kenya shows us something of how we were then: how we came to make a life on the African savannah, toting stone blades, living amid thundering herds of zebra and antelope (archaeologists found our toolkits lying in the same soils as their butchered bones).

When we made that step in Namibia—when our ancestors (cautious, bold, hungry, lost, who knows) first took to the arid plains of the ancient pro-Namib semidesert—we were caught, from the very start, in the fierce focus of raptor eyes.

If you have seen a bird, T. H. White once wrote, *it has already seen you*. This counts double for raptors. The glossy dark eyes of hawks, buzzards, falcons and vultures, front-facing and shielded from the sun by stern bone brows, are typically between two and eight times as powerful as our human eyes. So those first proto-human hunts, those early foraging expeditions among the corkwoods and acacias, might have been watched over by, let's say, a lappet-faced vulture, spiralling high up in the eye-watering blue overhead (a vulture's beady eye could pick out something as lumbering as a hominoid from miles away)— or perhaps a jackal buzzard, looking up from a killed cane-rat or found zebra carcass, seeing us, and loosing off its yelping dog's call. Maybe a rock kestrel, from its perch on an outcrop, watched us approach, and watched the fat crickets go leaping upwards from the plants we disturbed with our sticks and feet.

Today, in those sunburnt Namibian scrublands, wintering rock kestrels tag along with foraging bands of chacma baboons. Humans and baboons are pretty distant relatives these days— a matter of some twenty-five million years, since our respective family lines came to a decisive fork—but baboons now do what our ancient ancestors surely did: they forage in busy family groups for food, plundering flowers, fruits and seed-pods among the sparse dry-season vegetation. The kestrels know the routine. With these clumsy primates come crickets and katydids, panicked into flight.

The Namib rock kestrels are close cousins of the European kestrel, *Falco tinnunculus*. The two species share a subdued, smart grey-and-tawny livery, sharp wingtips sheathed in black; both have a scouring eye and both deploy a sustained hover—bowed head still, small body struggling to reach terms with the wind—before stooping for a kill.

In western Europe we have long known kestrels as motor-way raptors.

Most of our main roads today are watched over by birds of prey. Over the M40 near the Chilterns it'll most likely be a red kite. Country highways of all kinds can furnish a buzzard, tail fanned like a conjuror's playing cards, wingspan flattened against the sky. You can see peregrines from the M621 as it coils through high-rise central Leeds. Perhaps from the B970 which tracks the Spey north-east you might see an osprey and mistake it for a dirty great gull (or, I suppose, see a dirty great gull and mistake it for an osprey)—you might, with luck, see a golden eagle, madly big, laughably big, from the A9 as it trims the southern border of the Cairngorms. The high silhouettes of raptors, glimpsed at the windscreen-edge or through an open sunroof—or from the backseat, maybe with a *look dad!* or a *blimey, mum, what's THAT?*—have a way of seizing our attention (does a part of us remember when we were prey?). I can't be alone in having found myself, when driving, dangerously distracted by a hawk-shape on the brink of eyeshot, and only snapping out of the trance at the warning growl of a nearside rumblestrip.

Kestrels were the only motorway raptors I remember from my childhood. That was before the resurgence of the buzzard in England and the re-introduction of the red kite—back when the peregrine was a totemic (but imperilled) wilderness species, rather than a standardbearer for the recolonising urban wild.

For the kestrel, the strip of grassland that skirts each high-speed carriageway, lazily kempt, rife with rosebay and hawthorn, is a killing field. On one side is a roaring river of asphalt and traffic; on the other, more often than not, something almost as inhospitable—an austere steppe of intensively farmed land, chromium-yellow with rapeseed, rough edges planed away by bromadiolone and theiametoxam, clothianidin and difenacoum. Studies have found that roadside verges offer better habitats for kestrel prey (voles, shrews, mice) than fiercely husbanded arable fields. The verge funnels the animals into the scope of the kestrel's gaze. It's a convenient package for the kestrel, which is agile enough to hunt within the confines of the strip. In addition to bustling rodent populations, the verge furnishes perching points—fenceposts, lampposts. This kestrel, like the rock kestrel of the Namib, conducts surveillance from a perch if it can; then—triggered by a twitch in the grass—comes the jump to flight, the hover, and the plunge.

We're doing now what we did back then. We cause an uproar, and the kestrels pounce. Back in the Pleistocene we trampled the plants and scared up crickets, now we lay down concrete and blitz the meadowland, but for a hungry kestrel it amounts to much the same thing: opportunity.

They must see us, watch us, from the same calculating perspective as they did two million years ago. We're still galumphing heavy-footed through the edgelands, causing havoc, small life scattering wherever we tread.

The field overlooked South Ferriby Cement Works, a dour bloc of interconnected sheds, shafts, cylinders and industrial units, starkly colourless, an exercise in industrial monochrome, as if someone had greywashed the lot in a paint called Uniform Smog or Faded Battleship. Steam or smoke rose from a thin chimney. The plant abuts the confluence of the rivers Ouse and Trent, where the Humber begins; across a narrow channel of turbid water is Read's Island, an eroding refuge for wading birds, and just a little way along the riverbank is the square-cut reach of bird-rich wetlands known as the Alkborough Flats.

There's the problem, Pete said. He wasn't pointing to the cement works. He was pointing to the ground beneath our feet.

Pete's an RSPB warden. The mutable waterlands of the Humber Estuary are his patch.

Nothing, he said. Stubbed the toe of his boot into the summer-hard soil.

This was a field-margin, the dirtbrown hem of a rectangular plot of cereal crop, and Pete was right, there was nothing there, just a strip of earth two feet across, as bare as the margin of this page. No timothy-grass or cocksfoot, no oxeye daisy, no yarrow, no knapweed. No grass, even. Nothing for insects or other invertebrates; nothing for birds.

The margin was land. Land is a resource. Land must not be wasted. Here in the shadow of the hedgerow it was being put to work as a *cordon sanitaire*, a no-man's-land keeping at bay the weeds, the wild.

Birds that have grown accustomed to life in our arable farmlands have always relied on the stuff that was never meant to be there—the stuff that thrived in the margins. Yellowhammers nested in tussocky microhabitats of grasses, fescues and bents; insects overwintered there, to be hunted out as chick-food in spring by grey partridges and tree sparrows; barn owls—and kestrels, on the day-shift—worked over the rustling vole-runs.

There was nothing here. No stridulation of grasshoppers, no swaying hum of bumblebees. A bird—a buzzard—drew my eye upward, and again in the middle distance I saw the cement plant, a grey fort in a lunar landscape. Earlier, Pete had told me about the little ringed plovers that nested there. The little ringed plover is a starling-sized wading bird that in the UK is known for its post-industrial tastes (the establishment of a British breeding population in the twentieth century was largely thanks to the proliferation of disused gravel pits). At the South Ferriby works, seasonal ponds have been dug out amid the industrial spoil; a little bit of room has been made, and the plovers have moved in.

There are farmers and land managers across Britain, of course, who make plenty of room, whose work is an accommodation with the wild, not a campaign against it. And of course not every cement plant rolls out the red carpet for breeding waders. But these bleached edges in our working countryside say something about how we see waste—how we think about the land we own, but can't make use of. Those awkward, idle meadow-corners; they'll always, for some, be squandered wealth, uninvested capital. Wilderness is wastefulness.

But waste is fundamental to what we are: messy eaters. All along the human food supply chain, birds have come to rely on the land we can't plough, the crop we can't harvest, the stuff we can't use (the discarded fruit husk, the spilled barleycorn, the unnetted pea-shoots, the past-its-use-by supermarket bread, the leftover doner kebab). This is the currency of our bargain with birds.

The arid limestone cliffs of the Judaean Desert are crossed by the shadows of migrating cranes and breeding Barbary falcons. A traveller here today might hear the dinky trill of the solitary desert lark (or it might by drowned out by the thunder of an Israeli Air Force F-15 on manoeuvres). Black mole vipers patrol the shadows. Where there's vegetation there might be Palestine sunbirds, chiffchaff-sized and black-to-bottle-green in the baking sun. This isn't, exactly, where it all began, but it's a place where we, the we of the Neolithic, left traces in the marl and sand, traces in which the early history of the birds' relationship with people can still be read.

Most of our ancient history is lost to us. Most of us, when we die, leave barely a trace. Our footprints fade, the echoes of our voices die away, the things we've built first crumble to rubble and then decay to dust. Our gravestones may stand for a century or two (they'll be perched on, sung on, shat on by generations of robins, blackbirds, thrushes, dunnocks). Our bones will most likely outlive the last memory of us, but they too will go in the end. We might, it's true, achieve a measure of permanence by decaying in just the right sort of palaeoenvironment, wet and unoxygenated, dense and undisturbed, and be changed, eventually, into stone, into fossils.

If the archaeologists of the far future are ever minded to come looking for us, what are the odds of their ever finding us—me, and you, and everyone we know? They're not good: it'll vary, of course, from place to place (fossilization is a geological lottery), but it's been estimated that about one bone in a billion achieves fossilhood, which means that the current UK population of sixty-six-odd million, with their two hundred and six bones apiece (give or take), is likely to leave a fossil legacy of… thirteen bones. Thirteen. Less than a handful (far less, in fact: the human hand consists of twenty-seven bones).

Everyone in your office, everyone who was on your bus to work, everyone in the queue at your local coffee-shop, everyone you passed by in the street, all those people—and then everyone they passed by in the street, and so on and so on, multiplying outwards, across city and suburb, field, fell and moor, this bookmaker in Warrington and this shop assistant in Gateshead and this radiologist in Falkirk and this schoolgirl in Yeovil and this software engineer in Haringey and you too, remember, wherever you are, reading this book—all this vast accumulation of busily rattling skeletons, and by the time those archaeologists of the far future arrive, there'll be nothing left for them to find, scattered across our hundred thousand square miles, but thirteen fossil bones.

It's the same for birds. This is the known unknown that we have to come to terms with: practically all of everything that's ever happened is gone for good and never left a trace behind; the bones and meat and feathers of pretty much every bird that ever lived has dissolved back into the earth, as fleeting and ephemeral, in the end, as a robin's song.

We have to remember this when we listen to stories from the early history of birds. The traces we've found of ancient bird-life are only that: only traces, and only what we've managed to find.

The rest is undiscovered. We can remember it at other times, too—we can remember it when we're walking in a wood, or on a beach, or by a river; we can remember that the earth beneath our feet, the sand or mud or leafmould in which we leave our short-lived footprints, holds within it an aeons-long history of living things; we can remember that, though there may be nothing written there that we can read, it's a chronicle, nevertheless, of thousands of years, millions of generations, of the birds' lived history. We can always remind ourselves that our relationship with the birds around us didn't develop in a single place, at one specific time; that wherever we are, it happened here too.

The cave complex at Q'umran, in that ancient Judaean Desert, has been occupied by people, on and off, for maybe ten thousand years. Those first tenants scraped new holes in the rock: today the complex is a mix of caves made by people and caves made by weather and geology. It was around here, in 1948, that a Bedouin boy discovered the collection of Hebrew and Aramaic scriptures later known as the Dead Sea Scrolls (*Search and seek and know what is sought by the dove*, urge the Testaments of the Patriarchs). The soft voices of rock doves have been heard here since long before the shouts and mutters and conversations of humankind: the oldest dove bones found at Q'umran date back around eleven thousand years. They're found in every prehistoric stratum and they're still there today, ducking Barbary falcons and intermixing with the feral birds of urban Israel (a colony in fact breeds on the old city wall of Jerusalem).

Q'umran is a rocky, crenellated habitat, the kind of place a rock dove would design for itself, given a free hand, so it's no surprise to find them here, but the distribution and condition of the dove-bones don't suggest that the doves we've found were simply lying where they fell. Rather, the bone-store seems mainly to have been accumulated by humans, for whom the birds were presumably a food source. Some of the bones—mostly shoulders and sternums—bore gnaw-marks and cut-marks; some had been burnt (that is, cooked). The proportion of burnt bones is greatest in the later strata, dated to the Copper Age, the Chalcolithic era, by which point the Neolithic Revolution was in full swing—we had mastered cultivation, or at least were promising apprentices.

For the birds, the doves and sandgrouse, sparrows and starlings, finches and buntings of the Fertile Crescent, we had opened a window on to a world of plenty.

Some revolutions are over in days (the bloodless coup, the palace seized by night). Others—the Industrial Revolution, say—stretch across a century or so, rackety, improvised, hungrily self-sustaining. The Neolithic Revolution began perhaps ten thousand years ago; it's generally said to have petered out, spent its momentum, around four thousand years ago, but the cut-off seems somewhat arbitrary—who's to say, really, that it isn't still going on? The turbulent millennia of the Neolithic Revolution saw the emergence of agriculture, and a transition in our relationship with food. The birds around us saw the same thing they'd seen before, humans and their waste, but this was on a new scale. The finches who watched over the first miller of Karaca Dağ as he stone-ground grains of einkorn wheat, the doves clustered on the cliffs above the first orchard-keeper at Gilgal as she tended her row of fig-trees—this was going to change their lives.

At Q'umran, we can surmise that our first steps in cereal cultivation brought a new dimension to our relationship with the cave-dwelling doves. They became drawn to us (or rather, to our crops), and we began to exploit them. We can imagine a new risk-reward strategy settling into place among the doves; we can imagine the early farmers watching the doves descend and reaching for slingshots, or drawing up trap designs. The Q'umran remains are just one early indication of the capacity of humans to adjust what ecologists call the *faunal association* around them—directly or indirectly, to steer and shape the lives of the animals and birds with which they share the landscape.

The skylarks hadn't been waiting for us, the turtle doves, the swallows, they hadn't been in stasis or limbo, their lives on hold until we came along with this transformative notion of 'farmland'. What we call farmland was familiar to the birds from long before we arrived.

Farmland is mainly a function of open space: in Britain, the birds grew up with open space. In the shifting climates of the

Pleistocene, before the Storegga landslip displaced Europe's continental shelf and the roaring North Sea subsumed the Doggerland isthmus linking England to the continent, the birds of this North Atlantic outpost knew a landscape of exposed steppe (the kind where demoiselle cranes dance and upland buzzards quarter the grassland in northern Mongolia today); their many generations fed, mated, reared chicks and died beneath cold, wide-open skies, on plains trampled and cropped close by woolly rhino, saiga antelope, giant elk and southern mammoth, grazing megafauna that laid down a sort of pasture atop the rising chalk and mulching peat.

When the land warmed in the interglacial lulls, savannah crept over the steppe, lush and fertile, shaded here and there by sparse, light-loving trees, grazed, now, and not gently, by straight-tusked elephant and European hippopotamus (this may have been when the blackthorn and hawthorn, their dense spines a defensive overkill in our world of nibbling deer, were first taught to sharpen up, and fight back). The birds knew a kind of meadowland before the woodland canopy closed in —and before the proto-agronomists of the Neolithic opened it out again.

We didn't invent lentils or vetch, we didn't come up with the idea of chickpeas, no neolithic Archimedes ever leapt from his tub with excitement at having discovered linseed; the birds were already well-versed in these things. What we altered, with our heavy brains and capacity to plan, were their concentrations in the landscape, their profusion, their availability, and their reliability. This is how we (farmers, now, landscapers, terraformers) shaped the lives of the birds.

More bird species—if not more *birds*—are specialists than generalists. We can speak, however loosely, about 'farmland' birds, 'moorland' birds, 'wetland' birds; godwits don't nest on sea-cliffs, quail don't feed in taiga, long-eared owls don't hunt over deserts, redstarts don't sing in reedbeds. Populations settle where the properties of a habitat fit the particular needs and particular skillsets of the birds. But we humans can be rather dull, rather blunt and slow, in seeing what those properties are—certainly when compared with the birds, who survey their surroundings on a micro-scale, immune to aesthetics, processing a sensory landscape stripped back to its essentials.

Sometimes, to see how the patterns of the world's birds warp and drift, mutate and evolve, we have to draw back the lens, imagine that we can watch these movements from the brink of the stratosphere or the terrace of the ISS—or we have to multiply the frame-rate, crank up the playback to cram the expanses of evolutionary or geological time into the limited compass of brains built only to accommodate minutes and hours and days. This stuff tends to be invisible in our time, 'real' time.

But we're nothing, we humans, if we're not tool-users, if we're not a species that's always figuring out how to be bigger, to extend our armspan, lengthen our reach. This isn't just a crude question of automobiles and bulldozers and jumpjets and *Aliens*-style power loaders, nor even—where we've sought to extend our senses beyond their inherent limits—of radiotelescopes and electron microscopes. *Data* is our superpower. More than any refracting lens or electromagnetic signal, data opens up new panoramas—with regard to birds (so often out of sight, out of range, in flight over empty places, so often just *beyond* us), it lets us see, really see, the unseeable.

For some, it's the arrival of the first swifts, tirelessly cutting helixes across a May sky high overhead. For some, it's the call of the chiffchaff, a crisp double chirp not far off the great tit's squeaky-hinge noise but at the same time a sound all its own, completely unique. It might be the swallows returning to their nest in the angle of the stable joists, or the sonorous diphone of April's first cuckoo ringing across the reedbeds. For me it's the song of the blackcap, what Gilbert White called a "sweet, wild note" and I call a shrill madcap jabber in the riverside trees, a volley of crackpot song rattling the new spring foliage, but whatever it is, it's a tangible token of bird migration—it's something we can see or hear, and it means they're back, the birds, from wherever they've been. But where *have* they been?

They don't tell us; they don't have ticket stubs or stamped passports, didn't send postcards, don't bring back souvenirs (unless we count the snatches of African birdsong the male marsh warbler brings home with him from Sudan or Tanzania to sing in his Kent rosebay thicket, as we might whistle a tune we remember from our holidays). Where have they been? All we can know, from those first silhouettes of swift or swallow, from those first wild warbler voices, from that crisp little ripple we feel quiver our hearts as the spring birds break upon us once again, is that they've been *somewhere else*.

The first solid datapoint we acquired in the context of bird migration was a crude one: a javelin of African hardwood, jammed through the neck of a white stork (later known as the *Pfeilstorch*, arrow-stork), which carried it to the German village of Klütz in 1822 and kickstarted our study of the journeys of birds. Now there are birds zipping across the world kitted out with geolocators and GPS tags that weigh less than a third of a gram—a 10g wood warbler can schlep about a 0.23g tag without being inconvenienced—but the principle is essentially the same. We take the data and we make maps; we open a third eye on the seasonal currents of birds.

We'll stay with the white storks—with the peregrinations of the white storks, bamboo-cane legs held out behind, long-fingered wings wide and barely bowed, cruising the vast migrant flyways each autumn from Europe to sub-Saharan Africa. Or not, as the case may be.

In 2013–14, researchers at the Max Planck Institute for Ornithology in Germany bugged the movements of these birds from breeding sites across Europe and north Africa: an infographic produced by Oliver Uberti for the book *Where The Animals Go* plots their southward routes like threads or rivers or fine veins crossing the Dardanelles, the Red Sea, the Strait of Gibraltar, a thick cable of flightpaths that frays only once the birds are over Africa and have diverged to their various wetland wintering grounds. But there are also lines that never go where the other lines go. One maps the autumn route of a stork from Germany, not south-east, to Chad, Sudan, Uganda, Ethiopia, but south-west, and not very far south-west—only as far as Rabat, on Morocco's Atlantic coast. There the stork settled down for the winter beside a landfill site (Morocco has upward of one hundred and fifty uncontrolled rubbish dumps). This is not the mighty migration we expect of our storks. Project lead Andrea Flack said that the typical landfill stork (*Mülldeponiestorch*, perhaps) doesn't do very much with its time except "get up, fly to the dump, stay there, and then fly back in the evening". The stork might well ask why it should be expected to do anything else.

Then there are the lesser black-backed gulls of Zeebrugge, another army of wanderers tracked by tech and mapped by Uberti. The LifeWatch team at Belgium's Research Institute for Nature and Forest are factory-scale accumulators of nature data, world leaders in modelling the churning tides of wild things. LifeWatch tags on 101 Zeebrugge gulls have blipped out 2.5 million GPS fixes (a data-scientist's eye view opens up to us the size, the sweep, the reach of birds). These gulls—cousins to the yawping and chip-thieving herring gull, and to the bull-necked greater black-back—trek up and down the Atlantic seaboard from the Low Countries to Senegal. A thick smear on Uberti's map shows a less *Lonely Planet*-friendly detour, made daily by dozens of gulls, from the Zeebrugge colony to a location off the Rue de la Bassée in Moeskroen: a refuse heap out the back of Roger & Roger, manufacturers and exporters of corn snacks and potato crisps.

"When you give gulls easy access to a giant pile of potato scraps, they take it", notes James Cheshire, Uberti's co-author. Well of course they do. Gulls aren't daft. But having this data visualised kicks us into seeing not just how our discards and surpluses shape the birds' day-to-day judgment calls (fly to Laayoune, Nouakshott, Dakar, or eat crisps in Moeskroen? Cross the Gulf of Suez, or—as many of Andrea Flack's storks did—loiter for the winter by a Tashkent fish-farm?), but how, like a pothole amid traffic or a commuters' train-station coffeeshop or a football on a schoolkids' playing field, they prompt reshapings, reorganisations, in the patterns of movement, patterns that are the titanic aggregate (millions of brains, tonnes of biomass) of those day-to-day decisions.

Food waste is farm waste—farm waste displaced, passed forward for processing, kicked a little way along the road, but still farm waste, and so the white stork probing for protein in the refuse heaps is behaving much like the silo-side sparrow hopping after spilt grain. Our food infrastructure is a global sprawl of habitats that wires together a million different micro-ecologies: not just the crows at the soybean seedlings, not just pink starlings in the plum-trees and mynas at the grapes, not just pelicans in the barramundi hatcheries, not just barn owls mouse-hunting in the cornfields and sparrowhawks snatching bluetits from the birdtable bacon-rind, not just the herring gull going at the styrofoam tray of chips, not just the magpie staking out the Biffa bins behind the supermarket, not just yellow wagtails catching flies in the footsteps of beef cattle, not just red-tailed hawks raiding chicken runs, not just reed buntings feeding on flies above sewage-farm filters, but all of these and a great deal more, thriving in the margins, the messy, waste-strewn edgelands of our food industry.

Vultures will strip what they can from a lion kill. Mockingbirds will steal food—dead lizards, heavy-bodied insects, dismembered birds—from a shrike's grisly thorn-bush larder. The burrowing owl uses the dung of grassland mammals to lure beetles. These birds, too, forage at edges of another species' food industry, but their operation is on a smaller scale, and on an *ad hoc*, gig-industry basis. As so often, what's come to exist between us and the birds already existed elsewhere; what makes it different is the scale of the operation. We industrialised our food production, because we could, which means that, really without meaning to, we industrialised the birds, too.

In the grasslands of south Kazakhstan, amid the yellow flowers of the Tarda tulip and the songs of white-winged larks, lives the little bird who opted out. This bird, *Passer domesticus bactrianus*, sidestepped the special relationship, the odd-couple plotline: *P. d. bactrianus* is the house sparrow that doesn't need a house.

Today, every other variety of house sparrow in the world is what's known as an *obligate commensal*. They need us, or, rather, they need year-round foraging in grain-stores and livestock feed troughs, and warm nooks between bricks, in broken gutters, beneath dislodged roofslates. Without us, they would perish. Our species is the house sparrow's habitat. Only *bactrianus*, of all the many house sparrow subspecies, lives independently of humans.

I grew up surrounded by house sparrows. My nineteen-eighties childhood in suburban Yorkshire was steeped in sparrow-chatter, accompanied by a hundreds-strong sparrow chorus, overlooked by the beady eyes of dozens of sparrow families who grew up in the gutters of our brick-and-sandstone semi. Sometimes we'd find a sparrow nestling dead on the patio, the orbits of its closed eyes a bruised baby-blue. Sometimes our cat (Sammy or Smokey or Bandit or Thomas) would struggle in with a live-and-flapping adult, which would clatter lopsidedly around the lounge until we managed to steer it out of the kitchen door. Once my dad backed his Datsun over an unwitting cock sparrow: I found it lying in the shadow of the rear tyre as if posed for a theatrical tableau, a thick ketchup splodge of blood on its grey breast. Sparrows bossed the bird table by dint of weight of numbers (only starlings—mobsters, looters, expert ruckers, a bird biker-gang, all elbows, beaks and catcalls—ever challenged their monopoly). If I hadn't known they were called house sparrows I might have guessed.

When we're children we grow up not just within homes, not just within families and communities, but within ecologies, too—encircled by clouds of birds, sharing the air with insects and pollen, our paths crisscrossing those of hedgehogs (we used to put out Whiskas for them) and mice (we used to put out traps for them); our lives are shaped and tempered by these living worlds, these embracing atmospheres into which each of us is born.

So house sparrows made me. Or helped to, anyway. It wouldn't be fair to hold them entirely responsible—but I can't think of another wild animal species (woodlice? House spiders? Cabbage white caterpillars?) that was so immediately, unavoidably present, so very there, when I was growing up; no-one but the house sparrows, in the gutters, under the rooftiles, on the peanuts, occupied such a cosy spot in my personal domestic ecology.

We have found, near Bethlehem, in the West Bank, the bones of a sparrow who lived its short life perhaps 400,000 years ago. It's not the first sparrow, it's just the first sparrow we know of—sparrows as a genus probably emerged in the savannah and semidesert of the Saharo-Arabian region in the Miocene, between five and twenty-three million years ago (for context, this was roughly when the apes were just getting going, too—

our far-off ancestors branched off from the chimpanzee line during the Miocene). That Bethlehem sparrow has been dubbed *Passer predomesticus*, a sparrow from before farmers and agriculture, before towns, before *us*, in the modern sense.

It's a strangely lonely thought. But of course the sparrows were doing all right by themselves. They didn't need us then; they had to *learn* to need us.

When the stirrings of the neolithic revolution began in the Middle East, let's call it 10,000 years ago, we think the sparrows were there; the dates, from archaeology and studies of sparrow genetics, seem to match up. They'd have been indifferent to us, when we finally arrived, with our first farming tools, our handfuls of seeds, our madly flowering dreams of plenty—like *bactrianus* today, or like some desert variety of linnet or redpoll. But they were about to be sucked into the machinery.

They grew as we grew. Within a few thousand years they were coupled with our revolution. The machinery did not chew them up; instead, they learned to use us, to occupy us like a shell. They couldn't control or direct us, but they didn't have to, because we kept doing exactly what they wanted: digging, sowing, growing, harvesting, threshing, storing (spilling, wasting, discarding). We built homes for them—we called the homes *ours*, but what would that matter to a sparrow? The datapoints of their movements came to correspond with the datapoints of ours; their patterns lined up with our patterns. As over the centuries the sparrows' habits ossified, becoming not just a behavioural quirk but something inherent in the sparrow, something non-elective—as the odd foray into the goats' pen, a few nights' roost beneath a roof tile, became not an option but an inescapable obligation—it might have looked as though the sparrow, now *domesticus*, now and forever the house sparrow, had lost (or surrendered) its independence. I don't think it had. I think, in fact, it had traded one sort of dependence for another—and had done pretty well out of the deal.

Is any bird really independent? Independent of us, yes— independent of the need for regular food, reliable shelter, no; independent of the imperative to stake out territory and breed, raise chicks, no; independent of the urge to *not die*, to not get shot, to not be decapitated by peregrine or snagged by wildcat, to not freeze, to not succumb to rain or snow or rising monsoon waters—no. For all our other failings, we're mostly a stable and reliable species (we're long-lived, and we stick around; our buildings—walls windproof, roofs rainproof—stand for generations; our cycles of agriculture remained the same for centuries). I think the sparrow struck a decent bargain in hitching its wagon to *Homo sapiens*.

We've always thrown stones at sparrows, sought to frighten them off, been at odds with them, as farmers and storekeepers, greedy about our grain. In Britain, on and off from the seventeenth century, reward payments were made by the parish for the killing of sparrows (these peaked around 1790–1800, with the threat of food scarcity looming; the last were made in the 1870s). Community 'sparrow clubs' were founded, bent on sparrow murder, and lasted into the twentieth century. It was not hard, as a rule, to keep a lid on the bird's numbers: they could be netted or shot easily enough. All of this made occasional dents in the farmland sparrow population, but in the sparrow's reckoning this was still a better bet than going it alone. By now, there was simply no prospect of the sparrows going without us, and very little prospect of us going without them (because the sparrows wouldn't let us).

And they're still with us. They're not as numerous as they were (and somehow they seem less cocksure, less resilient, less indestructible as a result), but they're still here. A farm isn't the same thing a farm used to be—nor is a farmhouse or a farmer's field, nor is a country town or a suburb or a city, but we must still be what we used to be, at least in part, at least in some of the ways that matter to the birds. This is why the sparrows stay.

One day, the meaning of us will change a little more, and then a little more, and there will come a point, one day, when we simply won't be the 'we' we were—we won't be the *Homo sapiens* the sparrows came to know, and then came to need, in the Fertile Crescent, ten millennia ago. Perhaps something new will come along for them. What might come along for us? That will depend on who might need whatever it is we provide—and *that* will depend on who we are; on what we become.

2. *Accidental Conservationists*

"Your scientists were so preoccupied with whether or not they could", says Jeff Goldblum's character in *Jurassic Park*, "they didn't stop to think if they should".

A lot of how we treat the wild things around us is bound up not just with what we want to do, and not just with what we feel we should do, but with what we can do, too. Often we do good only because we don't have the means or the knowhow to do bad. For much of our history, humans have been accidental conservationists.

It would be nice to think that, in pre-industrial societies, before cars and concrete and capitalism came along, humans were able to live in a state of ecological balance with non-human nature. But the idea soon butts up against the evidence. The history of island ecologies (so often such unique, precious and fragile things) provides a bracing corrective, with the right framing: 'before people' and 'after people'.

Consider New Zealand. When the first Polynesian settlers ran their boats up on to the shores of these outpost islands of the south-east Pacific, late in the thirteenth century, they were islands stalked by moa, hulking birds with long bowed legs and s-bending backbones, three metres tall when they wanted to be, capable, we think, of resonant, far-carrying calls, like the baritone piping of cranes. There were around 50,000 of them, nine species, six genera, ranged across the New Zealand archipelago; as they hauled up their canoes, those first Māori must have heard the calls of the moas chiming in the damp forest air. Perhaps they found their foot-long fleur-de-lis footprints in the wet sand.

They—that is, we, humans, hungry *Homo sapiens*—did for them all in just over two hundred years.

There were probably a few hundred people in that first landing-party, that founding Māori community. They, their families and their descendants took the land of the long white cloud by storm. The human occupation of New Zealand has been characterised as a 'chaotic colonisation', the new pioneers fast-moving and highly mobile, a guerrilla outfit of scouts and outriders, clever, strong, resourceful and hungry. This wasn't a wave-front of gradual expansion, but something more like a firestorm (it's an apt analogy: fire was the colonists' principal weapon in the war they came to wage on the New Zealand wilderness; almost all the lowland woodland of both the North and South Islands was razed within a half-dozen settler generations).

It isn't fair to call this a *war*. There was no enemy, except for those tireless old foes hunger, fear, exposure and death. These first New Zealanders sought to survive, not to destroy. Evolution and happenstance had given them the advantage over the islands' ecological status quo and they used it: their world grew a yard outward with every footstep, and at the same steady rate the world of other things—of birds, plants, mammals, insects— grew smaller, reduced in possibility, the odds revised, the dice tampered with.

A great deal followed from our capacity to occupy space, to push our boundaries outward, to overwhelm the landspace of other species. The transformative *blitzkrieg* that the Polynesians visited on the mediaeval New Zealand ecosystem was, remember, the work of the descendants of just a few boatloads of people. It raises, in retrospect, the question of what else we might have done, elsewhere and in earlier times, in making room for ourselves—what other erasures we might have been responsible for.

If we could watch the prehistoric creep of our species across North America, for example, like the dragline of an excavator or the bucket of a dredger along a seafloor, we might see landscapes being scraped clean of large mammals, large birds, large anything; we might see habitats hollowed out as we shoulder our way in. We might see vacant space bloom across the continent, an aura of emptiness surrounding our species.

Wherever archaeologists have looked for signs of prehistoric human impacts on large predatory species, they have found them. It seems to be what we do, what we've always done—and we can do it without disaster capitalism, without corporate adventurism and shareholder greed; we're perfectly well equipped to do it without any lumbering techno-economic infrastructure at all, perfectly capable of wreaking handmade artisanal havoc at a community level. There's very little evidence that small-scale human societies do anything much to prevent or mitigate the depletion of natural resources or the degradation of natural habitat—except, of course, what they achieve accidentally, simply by *being* small-scale.

Humans have changed since the Paleolithic, of course, and since the mediaeval age, and since last year, last month, last week—but this component in our makeup, this capacity for flailing, lunging, grasping outgrowth, seems still to be with us. These are the people who came splashing ashore on Te Waipounamu in the dying days of the thirteenth century; these are the people whose trampling across forest, heath and swamp (to build, to trade, to profit, to multiply, to eat, to live) now threatens eighty-odd per cent of the world's endangered birds. This is us.

About seven hundred of the world's bird species are listed as 'endangered' or 'critically endangered'. You can get a bit of perspective on that number by looking at the British List, which includes every bird species that has "been recorded [in Britain] in an apparently natural state at least once since 1 January 1950", plus a few incomers and outliers. That list in total includes about six hundred and fifteen birds.

So imagine if every bird you'd ever seen on UK soil, or in the UK sky or on UK waters, singing in a Welsh oak tree or feeding in Scottish silt or soaring over an English heathland, was in danger—that is, was facing *a very high risk of extinction*. A whole country's worth of birds, pretty much every bird that ever tasted the air over our archipelago, scrabbling on the brink.

For most people—including me—seven hundred is a lot more bird species than they could name (indeed, many of these severely endangered birds sound, to a provincial English ear, a bit made-up: gorgeted puffleg, purple-backed sunbeam, Newton's fiscal, western bristlebird, I mean come on). Most of those seven hundred are where they are (i.e. finding it harder, each day, to live, eat, migrate, breed, survive) because of us. Same old us. Same old expansive, ambitious, reckless, feckless us.

If the development of living things were planned, sketched out in advance, a matter of foresight and sober judgment, it might have been thought a mistake to let us have guns.

Picture a landscape of numbers, a scrolling landscape of digits ranged across three dimensions, to each square inch a number, a 0.23 or a 0.98 or a 0.01 or a 0.45. This is a way to see the world birds see, a world of probability values, of in-play odds perpetually recalculated (the brain of the bird a tireless bookie's clerk). To live on the edge is to navigate at every step a treacherous topography of risk. It's not just birds who do this, but all wild things (they all live on the edge, shunted out there by natural selection's centrifugal force), and not only wild things, but people, too (a soldier in combat, a gymnast on a beam, a pilot in turbulence, a boxer in the ring). Hominids have always been a factor in the birds' on-the-wing guesstimations—clubs and traps, and then javelins and arrows, the opportunities of the middle sky reconfigured (0.4s—you'll probably live—tripping over to 0.6s—you'll probably die)—but it was in the sixteenth century that we really began to reshape the birds' risk landscape. We extended our influence not only outward but upward.

The matchlock or arquebus, Tudor-era military hardware drafted into service in the English meadowlands, was at first only a single-shot threat, deployed mostly in target-shooting and the pursuit of four-footed game; the transformative step was taken when we began to stuff these cumbersome guns with multiple shot ('haile-shotte', literally a hail of lead), which of course for the birds—rook, partridge, lapwing, chough, cormorant, heron, hawk, whatever, indiscriminacy was built-in—sent the numbers spinning wildly. An Act of 1548 sought to restrict the use of hail-shot ("wherby an infinite sort of fowle is killed and much gaym therby distroyed"): aside from anything else, it made things too easy, and did nothing to hone the marksmanship of the soldiery. In England, in the 1560s, a gunman might be licensed to shoot upwards of twenty-five different bird species.

The open skies had become a killing field. The birds' safe space wasn't so safe any more; their world had shrunk, the odds in their favour diminished. By the 19th century, 'market hunters'—bird traders, whose business was premised on hunting in bulk—were using huge, boat-mounted 'punt guns': one of these, 'Irish Tom', 300lb, fourteen feet from muzzle to stock, had the capacity to bring down more than a hundred birds with a single shot; a hunter in the US claimed to have killed four hundred and fifteen ducks in one broadside from a battery of four punt guns, and around a thousand in the course of the night's hunt. This sort of thing wasn't just a new danger for the birds, it was a fundamental alteration in the condition of their habitat (indeed their stronghold): guns literally changed what the sky was.

Setting aside the wrongs or rights, this is humanity in microcosm: going further, doing more, taking more, just because it can. There's nothing uniquely human about that—but our many points of overlap with the birds, coupled with the breadth and strength of our grip, mean that the birds have had to rebuild themselves, redraw their patterns, redirect their currents, to fit; again and again they've had to shift over, to move just a little further out of our reach.

The species that made such short work of the moas, that leveraged the late-mediaeval military-industrial complex to scale up bird-killing to a mass-production level, now, of course, has the power—the technology, the finance, the economic motivations—to level wildernesses, to deforest on a continental scale, to reinvent entire landscapes in brick, steel and concrete.

And yet, there are still places over which we don't have power, that we can't control, can't subdue, even though we might want to. We are some way on from the late stone age, but we still have limits. It isn't that we don't have the tech, don't have the tools—of course we do (often the tools are much the same as the ones we had back then, but scaled up, souped up, beefed up: tools for cutting, clearing, killing, levelling). Our limits now take other forms.

One is a lack not of resource but of will. Beyond this limit we find dereliction, neglect, the spaces we simply can't be *bothered* to reinvent. So we end up with, for instance, the square quarter-mile of cracked concrete between the river and the railway line in the heart of Leeds, in northern England, which I pass on the train most days: there was an ironworks there once, I gather, and then it was a car park, and they used to hold car boot sales there. Now there's nothing, other than a walled-off oblong of crowding elder, ragwort, sorrel, white-belled bindweed and buddleia, the plant Mark Cocker has called the "dominant botanical motif" of this kind of unintended wilderness. The motivation to do something here—financial, or moral, or whatever else—just doesn't exist.

On a bridge across the Leeds-Liverpool canal just outside the town of Shipley, where I live, someone has stencilled the slogan NATURE RESERVES R 4 PEOPLE WHO ARE BLIND TO NATURE, which is rubbish, but it does draw your attention, as you walk on, to the non-reserves, the tracts of unofficial countryside, that occupy the canal banks. There are the deserted backyards of unlet business premises, raggy with nettles and bramble, lively with birdsong. There are the derelict industrial units (WEAK ROOF, GUARD DOGS PATROL) that always have a collared dove on the roof-ridge or magpies bickering in the busted guttering. There are the ages-old waterside warehouses whose corrugated-iron loading bays tremble with the lowing snores of roosting pigeons. There's the squarish stretch of skewbald-green concrete where something big once was and now there's nothing bar driveways that go nowhere and finches picking over the weed-heads. There's a disused outflow pipe (I hope it's disused) where a wren has made a nest.

You can find these places everywhere. They're the awkward-shaped lots where no-one can profitably build, the gaps between railway lines, the concrete footings of abandoned construction projects, the contaminated brownfield no-one can afford to clean up. We can peer in at them through rusty railings, or over the tops of brick walls (because they're still *property*, after all). We can tell ourselves that we *could* make good use of these places, if we wanted—but that, looked at straight, is just *can't*, phrased differently.

They're not quite havens for birds, these places, these abandoned squares of city or suburb, they're not perfect, even by the birds' lights: they're dry, save for shallow and short-lived puddles after rain, and they're often floored with concrete;

the air here, no less than elsewhere in the city, is soupy with particulate pollution. But they are quiet, sheltered, and thick with vegetation (give or take the biannual depredations of contractors with strimmers and plastic visors)—they are good places for insect-eaters to feed and nest and sing.

They're places where we can't go and the birds can. We fell away and they—goldfinches at the thistles, blackcaps rattling out songs from buddleia-tops, blue tits picking caterpillars from elder leaves, gulls chasing spiders across the graffiti-scrawled brick walls—moved in.

Elsewhere, we find that we've imposed limits on ourselves: we've outsmarted ourselves, talked ourselves into situations we can't find our way out of. We've made monsters we don't know how to fight. So in these places, again, we're accidental conservationists, preserving habitats because we've made it too hard for us to trash them.

We certainly had a good go at trashing the habitats on the banks of the Pripyat river, which tracks the Ukraine-Belarus border eastward through miles of damp forest and drenched wetland. Much of this land is rich is birdlife. The vast Pinsk marshes, which hem in the Pripyat before it bends southwards toward Ukraine and the Dnieper, are home to a diverse stew of wetland species: black and white storks leggily patrol the shallows; rails—spotted crake, little crake—lurk in reedbeds; breeding little gulls and white-winged terns raise a racket as they bob and swoop in the middle air; Terek sandpipers and great snipes probe the sphagnum bogs for soft-bodied prey, while overhead other kinds of predator quarter the marshes—greater spotted eagle, white-tailed eagle, black kite. Capercaillie territories are staked out in the understorey of the fringing woodland and the songs of barred warblers, azure tits and collared flycatchers dance over the resonant bassline of drumming white-backed woodpeckers.

We've been tampering with the Pinsk marshes for a while. A state-sponsored expedition of 1872 constituted the Russians' first attempts to 'reclaim' these thriving wetlands (*drain the swamp* is not a new political motto, though it was once less figurative than it has been in recent times). In the marshes' eastern reaches, wide tranches of sodden loam and moss were choked off and dried out, seized by farmers for pasture; the Soviet years—especially the latter decades of the twentieth century—saw further drainage, the marshes' lifeblood diverted into reservoirs and culverts, low-growing greenery stripped, the wetland made safe for cows and sheep and Agromash tractors.

Further downriver, though, we're done with tampering, at least for the time being. After its turn southward the Pripyat river passes into a new kind of nature reserve, the Polesky State Radioecological Reserve. This is Chernobyl country. The number four reactor at Chernobyl blew up in April, 1986, the worst disaster in the history of nuclear power generation. A swath of north Ukraine and southern Belarus was showered with radioactive fission products (as were, to a greater or lesser extent, the rest of us, as the fallout plumes were drawn into the intercontinental airstreams).

The Soviet 'nuclear city' of Pripyat, built to house the Chernobyl plant and its workers, is a ghost-town now, its thirty-odd thousand citizens evacuated as the radionuclides rained down. Newspapers occasionally run photographic spreads on it: Pripyat's deserted fairgrounds, abandoned schools, empty and echoing public swimming baths. We can't live there any more. The land around it, for *miles* around it, is a nature reserve by default.

The birds of Pripyat watched over our exodus. They saw us go. They suffered, we think, or anyway they changed—a study has shown that birds exposed to the background radiation left by Chernobyl have less-developed brains than average. But then, remarkably, they may have adapted: research in 2014 suggested that local birds—red-backed shrike, great tit, swallow, tree pipit, black redstart, hawfinch, four kinds of warbler, three kinds of thrush, two kinds of nightingale—had developed increased resistance to the genetic damage associated with exposure to ionizing radiation.

This chapter, though, is about our withdrawals, our holding-back, not the harms we've done but our inadvertent doing-no-harm. As our footsteps have faded from the land around Pripyat, as our signal, coded in the molecules of caesium-137 and strontium-90, has died away, the non-human has not exactly *returned*—it was always there; it always is—but has changed, moved in a new direction, responded to the pressure-shift.

There's a vituperative dispute among scientists who study the Chernobyl no-go zone over how much the place has recovered, to what extent it has regenerated and rewilded itself. On the one hand there are those who maintain that the zone remains an irradiated wasteground, that the populations of wild things there remain stunted and impoverished, that—contrary to the *National Geographic* spreads—this is no safe haven, no animals' playground, but only another badland, toxified by human folly. Then there are those who argue that, beyond the torched hotspot of the Pripyat-adjacent Red Forest, radiation levels in the zone are, as these things go, relatively low; there are those who point to the roaming wolfpacks of Polesky, to the boars and raccoon-dogs seen ambling by the researchers' camera-traps in the South Belarus woods, to the eagle owl, extremely scarce in Ukraine, spotted dozing on an abandoned excavator near the concreted 'sarcophagus' that encloses the Chernobyl plant. "There are birds flying in and out", researcher Konstantin Checherov told documentary-makers in 1996. "The sarcophagus has a life of its own." A white-tailed eagle was captured and radio-tagged by biologists within a few miles of the meltdown site. Eurasian cranes are no longer rare here. Veteran Chernobyl ornithologist Sergey Gaschak has logged 249 bird species within the exclusion zone. "Nobody wants more radiation", Fred Pearce has written. "But many animals don't like people either."

For us, in this chapter, Chernobyl's radioactive legacy is really a side-issue. For us, the Chernobyl Exclusion Zone is above all a study in human abandonment, an opportunity to consider the lives of birds—their movements, their motivations—in a landscape emptied of people. Entombed Chernobyl and the grown-over ghost-city of Pripyat offer a darkly evocative rein-forcement of the idea that places built by humans don't have to be human places. When the humans are gone we can see with a clearer eye what it is that the birds see when they look at the things we've built.

There's something in all this that smacks of a post-Apocalyptic movie concept: in the idea of the denuded Red Forest, we can see *The Road* (2009), all birdsong digitally stripped from its soundtrack; the Pripyat wolves recall *The Day After Tomorrow* (2004), where a climate shutdown brings hungry wolfpacks to Manhattan; the vision of a post-human wild kingdom brings to mind the tumbledown city given over to zoo animals in *Twelve Monkeys* (1995). We're fascinated by what might one day live where we once lived.

It's easy to imagine that when humans are removed from a place it's as though a stopper has been pulled from a plughole —to imagine the birds pouring in in a spiralling cascade, filling up the vacuum with life in a new shape. But our lives and those of the birds are not just transparencies overlaid on one another; we're interlinked—as we've seen, we're both embedded in the same landscapes, and extricating one can't always be done without making a mess of the other.

It's true that birds of woodland and scrubland will do well enough as these habitats creep season by season to cover Pripyat's concrete and oxidized iron, but this stretch of Ukraine-Belarus was in part farmland, too, a generation ago. If there are no people there are no farmers, and again the balance of the landscape will tilt. And so white storks have ceased to breed near Chernobyl (white storks like pasture and shallow wetland, and avoid areas of overgrowth); barn swallows—the same sort of swallows we welcome back to Britain each spring—have declined as the farmland insect biome has been displaced. So it hasn't been only an inrush, but we have seen that, where we're forced to relax our grip—to truly let go, as we do almost nowhere else, and almost never willingly, and without rights of visitation, supervision, oversight—the bird populations breathe more freely.

There are other stories along the same lines. The 1957 Mayak disaster—an explosion at a weapons-grade plutonium plant that spat a radioactive dust-plume across a hundred square miles of Siberian farmland—created ghost-villages and ghost-farms, miles of ghost-road. Today, nettles grow waist-deep in the streets (it's hard, sometimes, considering these stricken places, not to think of the stories of mediaeval villages depopulated by the Black Death, where chronicles tell of grass growing long in the cart-tracks). Over two years of brisk state evacuations a wilderness grew out of the human landscape. This was already a brutalised place; with the Soviets on a permanent war footing, workers at the Mayak plant had been directed to discharge nuclear waste products straight into the Techa river. After '57 the relationship pivoted; the land, irradiated and toxic, now held the whip-hand, and we backed down, leaving the surroundings of Mayak in a state of profound and peaceful dereliction.

Today the contaminated zone is a thriving Ural nature reserve of grassland and birch forest (but you must never eat the mushrooms). People won't return in any numbers for at least another hundred years, and birds are present in startling profusion. Biodiversity here, according to one study, "sharply exceeds biodiversity of adjacent regions"; one hundred and seventy-one bird species—seventy-three per cent of all species ever recorded in this part of the world—have been ticked off within the park. Again, there will surely have been complications, perhaps some subtractions, a general recalibration in which species accustomed to the structures, textures and micro-ecologies of working landscapes found themselves at a disadvantage, but it's important to remember that that's how *everywhere* works.

"The historical perspective", writes the biologist D. R. Foster, "underscores the fact that wildlife assemblages at any given time are comprised of species undergoing strikingly different trajectories". While some populations flourish, others decline. Ecologies aren't monolithic, and can't be acquired wholesale.

The Soviet pseudoscientist Trofim Lysenko, wildly rewriting the principles of botany in the 1940s, insisted that seedling trees would pitch in to help one another, like good Marxist-Leninists, in common cause against weeds (Lysenkoism underpinned the launch and then the failure of the Great Stalin Plan for the Transformation of Nature)—but that's not how wild things really tend to work: the success of one species often has a bitter counterpoint in the form of another's decline, a good spring for this bird often a bad one for that. Ecologies maintain multiple narratives; they have to be mapped across time as well as space. Dynamism, fluidity, are built in.

Mayak and Chernobyl have been abandoned as a form of past-proofing, a long-term quarantining designed to insulate the people of today from the bad luck and recklessness of the past. The cranes of Korea benefit from something more like future-proofing. These cranes, white-naped and red-crowned, *Antigone vipio* and *Grus japonensis*, are both vulnerable species (the latter desperately so, its existence a matter of a mere three thousand or so birds); vulnerable, too, are their habitats, the things they need: saltmarsh, sedge, wet grassland. On the Korean peninsula the South Korean economy, geared for eternal growth, offers little slack, little leeway—like the machinery of intensive agriculture, it's engineered to force the margins ever tighter. But there are places where even Korea Inc. stops short, afraid of what might happen should it proceed.

The people of South Korea, Eric Wagner wrote in the *Smithsonian Magazine* in 2011, see North Korea as "like a fault, or a volcano, or some other intermittent, potentially cataclysmic phenomenon over which they have no control" (which isn't, by the bye, a bad way of thinking about how birds see us). A two-and-a-half-mile demilitarized zone (DMZ), buffered in its turn by a civilian control zone (CCZ), has been staked out between the two countries since the *de facto* end of the Korean War in 1953. It's littered with tank traps, riddled with tunnels, studded with perhaps a million landmines, and in this sense the DMZ is a military-historical artefact, but the real danger of trespass here has to do with the future, with what two rival nation-states, butting up against one another without mediation, might feel compelled to do. The DMZ is security not against the mistakes of the past but against the mistakes we haven't made yet.

Anyway, it's working out for the cranes. Where the unpeopled DMZ exists—think of it, perhaps, as a green ridge rising from uninhabitable desert—they make their wintering grounds, in the Panmunjom Valley and the Cheorwon basin (Cheorwon, half-DMZ half-CCZ, is the off-season home to more than two thousand migrant storks).

Conservationists fear what peace might mean here. The same is true on Cyprus, where a no-man's-land known as the 'green line' keeps apart the island's Greek and Turkish factions, and where lapwing, Calandra lark and stone curlew—all struggling outside the protected corridor—flourish in a mosaic of Mediterranean scrub, grassland, upland and tumbledown villages. "Redevelopment of the buffer zone should take into account the risk of even further losing the habitat of species already endangered", ecologist Nicolas Jerraud warned, as UK-brokered peace talks began on Cyprus in 2017. Of Korea—where reconciliation remains improbable in the short term, despite the summit of spring 2018—crane conservationist George Archibald worries that "if and when North and South Korea reunite, the development pressures on the DMZ are going to be severe".

Peace and war shape ecosystem outcomes in other ways. In 1914, as western Europe lumbered toward total war, a perverse sort of peace settled on the uplands and farmlands of Britain. The gamekeepers' guns—a strident, persistent, barking voice in the biophony—quietened. There were around 22,000 gamekeepers in Britain before the war; after, only around 12,000. By 1945 and the end of the second world war, there were perhaps 5,000. This wasn't all down to warfare (Lloyd George's inter-war land taxes hit many smaller game estates hard), but it was certainly the case that the gamekeepers' grip on Britain's bird life loosened while we were at war. Sparrowhawks, fierce and scrappy prey-birds of forest and farmland-edge, flourished during both global conflicts. The golden eagle population staged a notable recovery during the war of 1939–45. These were not amnesties or truces, no-one had signed a treaty, there was no non-aggression pact between the keepers and the raptors; our reluctant staged withdrawal from the field did not usher in any sort of predator golden age, but only shifted the balance a bit—only eased the pressure on certain populations for a little while.

There's no point, really, at which the life of birds becomes easy. Mortality is always fearfully high (a study of sparrowhawks from 1909 to 1949 estimated that more than two-thirds died before the end of their first summer of life). Bird life is itself a warzone. It's hard to imagine that any sparrowhawk—or any eagle, or any hen harrier—would really *notice* that there were fewer men with guns, fewer nests pulled down or trodden underboot, fewer sharp shotgun reports ringing in the skies of Norfolk or North Yorkshire. But still, we went away for a while, and the birds did better. The balance tilted. Peace, when it came, was not a universal peace.

It's best, for the birds, if we remain sundered, as a species—best if, hamstrung by fear and mistrustfulness (of ourselves, as much as of the people across the border, over the hills), there are places we daren't occupy, must never set foot in. When we're at peace—as in the biblical story of Babel—we build. When we're divided the tower remains unbuilt, or derelict, or falls into ruin. The Cypriot village of Varisheia, deserted by its people, its weeds now grazed by rare mouflon sheep; the gutted buildings of Cheorwon, on the south side of the Korean border, over which the red-crowned cranes pass each autumn—these are our towers of Babel, lost, grown over, repossessed, because we can't find common ground.

All of these stories are about power. They are also about what's known as *epiphenomenal conservation*—incidental, accidental conservation. I have never taken Anthony Joshua's WBO heavyweight title from him, I have never knocked Roger Federer out of the US Open, I have never pipped Magnus Carlson to the chess world championship, and I daresay I never shall, but do I ask for thanks? I do not, and not (only) because I'm an exceptionally magnanimous individual; it would, of course, be absurd to do so, just as it would be for us, as a species, to take credit for the eagles of Chernobyl, the winter cranes of the Korea DMZ, the whooping lapwings of the Green Line—and the same goes for the birds, animals and plants of our unmanaged edgelands, our lost acres of concrete and brownfield, our empty mill-buildings and derelict factories, our city wildernesses.

Nature reserves and national parks exist on sufferance. They're an expression of our human capacity for tolerance, a Good Thing on the whole but at the same time something of a fudge, idealistic in principle but on a species scale subject to something grudging and conditional. The prospect of *development* hangs over most of our wild places as the sword hung over Damocles. Wild things lease these places from a capricious landlord. *They're yours*, we say, *until we need them back.*

Theoretically, the same is true of our accidental wildernesses—one day, the *when* a question of atomic half-lives and unstable geopolitics, we'll probably recolonise the Polesky State

Radioecological Reserve and the DMZ and all the rest—but the difference lies in the power balance. These are not grace-and-favour reserves. They are not in our gift.

The science-fiction writer Bruce Sterling envisages a global archipelago of "involuntary parks", "a new kind of landscape", uninsurable, unexploitable, allowed "by government fiat" to overgrow. To the places discussed above Sterling adds abandoned military test ranges, "very old and decaying railroad lines" in the US ("which, paradoxically, contain some of the last untouched prairie ecosystems in North America"), and toxic-waste dumps, "whose poisons legally discourage humans but not animals".

"They bear some small resemblance", he writes, "to the twentieth century's national parks":

> "But the species mix is no longer natural. They are mostly fast-growing weeds, a cosmopolitan jungle of kudzu and bamboo... They are not representatives of untouched nature, but of *vengeful* nature, of natural processes reasserting themselves in areas of political and technological collapse. An embarrassment during the 20th century, Involuntary Parks could become a somber necessity during the twenty-first."

But this isn't quite right. It seems perverse, really, to watch this sort of *reassertion*—ragweed shoots breaking up old asphalt, starlings colonising abandoned towerblocks—and still think in human terms, to think that this is somehow about us: vengeance, nemesis, comeuppance, an eco-parable staged for our moral benefit. It's a plant finding new routes to light and water. It's a bird finding an undisturbed place to sleep or lay eggs. It's living things finding ways to be. We don't enter into it, either figuratively or literally (that's sort of the point). Being cosmopolitan doesn't make you unnatural; wild things are citizens of nowhere, or perhaps of anywhere. Some other things that aren't unnatural: concrete, iron, brick, glass, cities, people, even airports or skyscrapers or oil rigs, even nuclear power stations (ask the kittiwakes that gather around the warm-water outflows at Dungeness). Perhaps these things wouldn't be here if we weren't here, had never been here, but this is the most academic of questions. We are here and the things we've made are here. Nature is about now. 'Natural' means us, too, if it means anything.

Involuntary parks embody our buying into the birds' code: not 'ours' and 'theirs', but 'can' and 'can't.' Where we can't, we don't.

"A world map of Involuntary Parks would be an interesting and perhaps enlightening addition to new maps of our newly uninsurable world", Sterling writes.

On a map of human doings, human goings, there are not—on land, at least—very many pockets of nothing. Those that do exist are islands, enclaves. In a world where we go where we please and do as we want, they have a special magic. Birds sing there and we don't hear them. These are the places where the map still says, *here be dragons.*

3. *Movements*

We might picture a person—a pretty clumsy person, a bit ham-handed, not especially deft or careful by nature—trying to carry, in their cupped hands, quantities of some fine-grained and uncooperative substance: sand, perhaps, or seed, or, better, ants or tadpoles or money-spiders. You'd expect some sort of general success—you'd expect to end up with at least some of the stuff that was *here* dumped over *there*—but also, you'd expect spillages, droppages, messy escapes, stuff ending up where no-one meant it to be, everything getting a bit out of hand.

That's us. For birds, for most of our history, one way or another, we've been agents of dislocation. And we haven't tended to be especially good at it.

When we move birds from one place to another, we often think of ourselves as doing something orderly, as being engaged in some kind of maintenance work, patching up holes, filling in gaps, being diligently janitorial. More often than not the reality is that we're introducing not orderliness but, on the contrary, an element of the random and chaotic—a positive gloss might suggest that we're keeping things interesting. The birds are (as they usually are) indifferent; they're great *copers*, are birds. But on an ecosystem scale our fumbled hand-offs can make a hell of a mess.

There are "wouldn't it be nice" introductions and there are "let's try that again" introductions and—most excitingly of all—there are "whoops" introductions (in the long run, they all have the potential to be "whoops" introductions). Let's go through them in order.

Ecologists today are very keen on talking about 'shifting baseline syndrome' as a means of explaining our resistance or blindness to ecological change. It's a form of normalisation: it says, the state of things *now* (or rather, the state of things twenty or thirty of forty years ago, when I was young and summers were long and we all climbed trees and scuffed our knees and holidayed in Scarborough and *I was young*) is the state of things as they should be. Shifting baseline syndrome looks out of the back window and says, *this is normal*.

So a post-war generation thinks that farmland without corncrakes is normal. A later generation thinks that peregrines in city centres are normal. An older generation thinks that it was normal to have the corncrakes but not the peregrines. Go back far enough and *of course* there ought to be snowy owls breeding among the glaciers of the West Midlands, *of course* there ought to be ancestral hummingbird *Parargornis* flickering through the forest glades of late-Palaeocene Kent.

There isn't really such a thing as *normal*. But shifting baseline syndrome makes us think that there is.

Our baselines are portable not only through time but through space, too: we can calibrate what's normal and right by reference not only to *now* but also to *here*. This is what we did when we came to a place of jungle and red desert, of laughing kingfishers and screaming parrots, and tried to fill it with skylarks.

The first western settlers in Australia found that the noises of the local birds were not to their taste. "There are several chirpers, a few whistlers, many screamers, screechers and yelpers, but no songsters among the birds here", wrote the naturalist Thomas Harvey in 1854. It was not enough for these alienated immigrants to bring in their baggage their own language and customs, their own civic structures and moral codes, their own books, gramophone records, paintings and musical instruments—all amounting, in essence, to one vast security blanket. They had to also bring with them their countryside—the countryside of home.

In one sense, the advocates of what became known as 'acclimatisation'—the introduction of new species, often on a huge scale—had no grasp at all of ecology (the scholar Thomas Dunlap has pointed out that they saw species as interchangeable "pieces" that existed against "the neutral backdrop of the land"; today we have a much stronger sense of landscape, habitat, as an active and dynamic agent in ecological processes). It wasn't obvious to them that ecologies millennia in the making are finely tuned machines, all hairsprings, zipping flywheels and delicate escapements, easily nudged out of true (for that matter, to judge us by our actions, it's not as obvious as it ought to be to us today, either). But in one sense they *were* aware that no species stands quite alone, that each is a part of the continent, a piece of the main—they knew this, because under that brutal Australian sun, among the "shadeless, grey, sombre-looking gum trees", heckled by wattlebirds and lorikeets, they *felt* it. These Englishmen were aliens.

And so the skylarks were shipped in, to alleviate—and to share in—the colonists' dislocation. Nightingales, too, were imported, released into Melbourne's Botanical Gardens, though none survived to sing through a second spring; blackbirds and thrushes, sparrows and finches, underwent the same extraordinary ordeal of transportation and transplantation. Few really took hold, though skylarks still sing over Tasmanian farmland. The appeal of 'acclimatisation' soon wore thin, anyway: as Dunlap puts it, "by 1880 the majority of Anglo-Australians were native-born, and for them Shelley's skylark and England's hedgerows were as alien as the woolen school uniforms they wore in Sydney's heat. Their childhood memories were the bellbird's chime and the kookaburra's laugh, the ragged silhouette of eucalyptus trees, the crunch and smell of their leaves underfoot." In other words, the new Australians had drawn a new baseline.

Unstowed from the cargo ship, released from its cage of ninety days or more, bathed in sudden sunlight, what might a skylark have made of freedom in a place like Australia? There's a phlegmaticism to wild things—unlike us, they haven't, as far as we can tell, acquired the habit of reflecting on circumstances. Of course the skylark would twig that it was no longer on its home heath, its hard-won English territory (skylarks are rigorously territorial). This might be a turbulent thought. Or perhaps its first idea would be to get away from the chaps in tweeds and moustaches who had trapped it and caged it, all those weeks ago—to find a safe spot somewhere. To *not die*: that, as always, would be the underpinning policy.

Living in a new ecosystem would be a learning process but then being alive is always a learning process. You emerge one day to find that the hawthorns are gum trees and the wheatears are budgerigars and the ocean is on the wrong side and the stars are all different—but, for all the skylark knows, this is a thing that happens to every skylark, sooner or later. The skylark, this skylark, has less chance of doing well here than it would have had back home, but really that's just a question of statistics. The skylark doesn't know it. The skylark has a can-do attitude.

The homesick proponents of 'acclimatisation' grew old watching their projects fail, their children and grandchildren come to love an alien countryside. The skylarks and nightingales and sparrows and blackbirds got on with things, meanwhile: with living, with dying, with breeding or not breeding—with just *being*. That's the tight focus. Pull back, and we see that humankind has shaken the kaleidoscope. Everything has got just that bit more complicated. We wanted to curate a nostalgic safari-park, an immersive living theatre of pastoral England, in the antipodes. What we made was and remains a mish-mash, a tossed salad of fusion ingredients. It's not *wrong*, exactly (there's no *right* ecosystem, just as there's no *normal* ecosystem, though of course we can question the motives that brought it about). It's just another instance where our strange, dancing patterns across the world map hooked arms with the patterns of birds, and drew them in a new direction.

"I'll have a starling shall be taught to speak nothing but 'Mortimer'", declares Sir Henry 'Hotspur' Percy, heir to the Earldom of Northumberland, "and give it him to keep his anger still in motion". The words are spoken in fury, Hotspur riled by the new-crowned Henry Bolingbroke. It's Shakespeare's only starling (the lines are from *Henry IV, Part 1*) but it's a starling whose offspring, speaking figuratively, would later darken the skies.

Sometimes an introduction is like a bomb going off. Sometimes the payload is hooked up to a slow-burn fuse. The ocean liner that brought Eugene Schieffelin's starlings from Europe to Manhattan made a slow, smouldering way west; the birds were docked, processed, transported by carriage the dozen blocks from the Battery to Central Park, and then released. The impact on the city wasn't immediate. Give it a few years, though, and —*boom*.

Schieffelin is the patron saint of wouldn't-it-be-nice bird relocations, a Quixotic New York pharmacist tied up with the American Acclimatization Society, the US rump of the same movement that took skylarks to Australia. The sixty starlings he set loose in the park that day in 1890 were part of a scheme to populate the States with every bird species mentioned in Shakespeare's plays. Why? Why not? Shakespeare's list runs to fifty species (skylarks are in there too, or at least *larks* are; the Bard never specifies the species). Most foundered in the New World. The starlings didn't.

At around the same time as Schieffelin the pharmacist was performing this grand experiment, W. H. Hudson in the "brick desert" of London was writing of his city's starlings gathering in autumn in Battersea Park, "until the trees... are black with their thousands, and the noise of their singing and chattering is so great that a person standing on the edge of the lake can hardly hear himself speak". In his novel *Antic Hay* (1923), Aldous Huxley described "innumerable flocks of starlings" sweeping across the sky over Paddington. It was no secret that urban starlings specialised in crowd scenes; Schieffelin and his fellows must —unless their research began and ended with *Henry IV*—have known what to expect. Perhaps they thought Manhattan could handle it. Perhaps they simply wanted to watch murmurations warping in the dusk over the East River, and let the rest go hang.

In a 1990 centenary profile, the *New York Times* characterised the starling as "one of the costliest and most noxious birds on our continent", detailing a rap-sheet that runs from devouring "vast stores" of seeds and fruit (guilty), "defiling" the city with faeces (guilty), spreading histoplasmosis, toxoplasmosis, and Newcastle disease (guilty), "rudely evicting" other cavity-nesting bird species (guilty) and bringing down aeroplanes (guilty: as the *NYT* reported, a Lockheed Electra crashed in Boston in 1960 after a flock of ten thousand starlings flew into its engines). There are perhaps two hundred million starlings in the US today. "Schieffelin's mission had become more appropriate to a work of Hitchcock than of Shakespeare", the newspaper wrote.

If this were a book about people rather than birds we would linger longer on Eugene Schieffelin, his strange dreams of Dunsinane's martlets at nest beneath the eaves of Hoboken brownstones, of the hedge-sparrow of Lear's fool dodging cuckoos among dogwood and black huckleberry—we'd spend a little more time with the New York druggist and his madcap visions of English birds under American skies. Would he, we might wonder, have regretted his reckless bargain with the wild? Perhaps he would think it all worthwhile, all the noise and shit and clamour, in return for the black-nacre gloss of a starling's summer primaries, the jabbering rooftop conversation (the catcalls, the impersonations, the swannee whistles), those twilight murmurations over the city, the reckless flush of *life* that starlings represent.

Eugene Schieffelin's hundred starlings arrived in New York in the middle of America's third great wave of human immigration. That, too, was a transformative transfusion, a hustling re-shaping of the urban identity (twelve million people—Irish, Norwegian, German, Russian, Jewish, Polish, Hungarian, British, Swedish, Italian—passed into New York City through the Ellis Island gateway between 1880 and 1930)—that too was a bracing wallop for the city's ecology. Both are now embedded, locked in to any realistic conception of the modern US city. We might wonder if Schieffelin saw any of it coming when he popped the latches on his starling cages that day in Central Park.

In the UK today it's perhaps hard to see the starling—no, *starlings*, always plural, multiple, multitudinous (they *sound* like there are thousands of them, even when there aren't)—as effacers, spoilers, defilers of clean streets, disablers of jet engines, because in recent years we've grown used to seeing them as creators of beauty; we've got to know their artistic side. Over Gretna Green, Ham Wall, Middleton Moor, Aberystwyth Pier, but most often of all on YouTube, Twitter and Facebook, we watch them throwing shapes against darkening skies, stippled auroras in shifting greyscale: *murmurations* (a once-obscure word we all now know, thanks to the starlings).

I can be especially sentimental about starlings because, on our honeymoon, four years ago, my wife and I watched them gather in the November twilight over the reedbeds at Leighton Moss. It wasn't a big murmuration, by the standards of the place (a west Lancashire wetland, once drained for agriculture, now protected for birds); just an assembly, a gathering together of birds ahead of the roost. They came zipping in in small squadrons, gliding sharp-winged on a smooth descending plane (I imagined the crackle of their intercoms: *reedbed in sight, squadron leader. Angels one, Leighton Moss, lowering landing gear. Roger, starling three. Over.*) As a lemon-yellow moon rose they performed intermittent sub-murmurations (murmurettes?)... I almost wrote *just for us*, as Frin and I were the only humans present, but of course it wasn't for us, or even in spite of us, but regardless of us. It was wonderful, anyway. We stayed until it was dark and the starlings had all settled into their reedbed roosting-places.

I don't think I thought at all about Eugene Schieffelin, but if I had I might have thought something along the lines of—*yeah, I get it.*

But let's stay with the starlings. In fact it took six years for the Schieffelin starlings—the sixty of 1890, and a further forty released in '91—to breed (the first pair chose the gutters of the Museum of Natural History in which to make their nest). Then, having attained critical mass, the population went nuclear, exploding to about fifty million by the middle of the twentieth century.

Their success in the US—which really wasn't anything radical, was just starlings doing what we know starlings do —might remind us that oceans are just inconveniences, that continental rifts don't mean anything in an ecological sense. It's true that cities simplify things: they act as base-camps, familiar biospheres built by armies of terraformers, implanting stuff we know in landscapes we don't (same smoke and brick, same starlings and pigeons—High Street homogeneity didn't begin with Starbucks and Gap). But when we enable introductions, as Schieffelin did, it's not a revolutionary act, even if the project then goes rattling out of hand, goes beyond what we might have imagined. The path of the transatlantic steamship that carried the pilgrim starlings to the East River dock might best be seen as a short-lived land bridge between the Old and New Worlds, an unstable isthmus that quickly rose and as quickly sank, but lasted just long enough for the birds to make the trip. Often, that's what we are, for them: waystations, stepping stones, tidal causeways, components of bridgework.

Boat or bridge, offshore rig or volcanic islet or weather buoy or coral atoll, it's all the same to a bird. Somewhere to pause, somewhere to breathe.

They don't always need a Eugene Schieffelin (or a Pierre Lorillard, pioneer breeder of English partridges in Jobstown, New Jersey, in the late 18th century, or a G. W. Wallace, one of the founders of a still-surviving expat skylark colony on Vancouver Island, British Columbia). Plenty of birds make it across the Atlantic under their own steam, which seems absurd, but then practically *all* bird migrations seem absurd (starting with the goldcrest, Europe's joint-smallest bird, which weighs five-and-a-half grams, about the same as a twenty-pence piece, and crosses the North Sea from Scandinavia each autumn, knocking off up to five hundred miles a day). A Baltimore oriole showed up in Scilly in September, 1999. Six red-eyed vireos came tumbling into Ireland in October, 2000. Cape Clear, at the southern end of Ireland, saw a yellow-rumped warbler in 2001. A white-throated sparrow was seen skimming the waves above Dogger Bank in May 2002 and in the autumn of 2003 a bobolink came to County Cork. Each year brings its own bright and unpredictable spattering of off-course North Americans.

Ornithologists, cross-referencing these vagrations with wind regimes and cyclonic flows, write cautiously in their reports of "ship-assisted" transatlantic journeys, almost as if the birds were engaged in an athletics event and their achievements ought to be marked in the logbooks with an asterisk, like a wind-assisted longjump or a marathon record set with a pacemaker. A white-throated sparrow rode from Newfoundland to the Kiel canal aboard a ship in 1998. Several Canadian snowy owls boarded ships at Greenland amid North Atlantic storms in autumn 2001, hitching to Suffolk and the Low Countries. This isn't an easy option for the birds—most stowaways perish before landfall ("for those surviving a full transatlantic passage", the biologist Norman Elkins writes, "the duration would be an ordeal, especially for small insectivores")—but it might be a better bet than the grey open ocean; of course, both scenarios are worse for the birds than keeping to their familiar flyways, avoiding the eastward surges of tropical storms and the blustering afterblows of hurricane season.

Consider the Scilly bufflehead. She made it from North America—probably somewhere on the eastern seaboard of the US—to Tresco in the Scilly archipelago in the winter of 1920. She would have been a fine-looking duck, cousin to the European goldeneye, an outsize round head on a dainty grey body, a smudge of white on each coffee-coloured cheek. At Tresco, she was shot by a wildfowler, and logged in the ledger: the first known UK bufflehead. There haven't been many more (a male at Foxcote in Buckinghamshire in 1961, another on South Uist in 1980), but the point is, there have been some. Other transatlantic ducks: blue-winged teal (Upper Nithsdale, 1858), American black duck (Kent, 1967), canvasback (Cliffe, 1996), white-winged scoter (Blackdog, 2011), harlequin duck (Filey, 1862, found dead, and now preserved for perpetuity in Mansfield Museum). Windblown and disoriented, they crash-landed on these islands like the knackered Vickers Vimy of Alcock and Brown touching down in a Connemara peat-bog in 1919: showing, if nothing else, that it can be done.

There's no ruddy duck, *Oxyura jamaicensis*, in this list of vagrant Anatidae, because as far as I know no ruddy duck has ever made the flight from its breeding grounds in the midwest US, or its winter resorts south of the Mason-Dixon, to the lakes and gravel-pits of the UK—but they were common here, nevertheless, within my lifetime. They got here via that *other* route, the route of cheats, short-cutters, interlopers: we brought them here. Then we exterminated them. But we ought to begin at the beginning.

At the start of this book I wrote about the importance of seeing ourselves as others see us. It's not something we're good at doing; if we'd been better at it, things might have turned out differently for the ruddy duck.

We gave the ruddy duck citizenship—that is, we added it to the British List, acknowledging that the species had established a sustainable wild population here—in 1971. Prior to that, within Britain, it had always been either a captive or an escapee. Ruddy ducks (they're called that because of the drake's rubicund coloration; he has a red-brown body, a stiffly upright tail, a black bandito-mask, and—most thrillingly—a bill of electric blue) were always considered hard birds to breed: pre-war attempts in Shropshire came to nothing, and it wasn't till the Wildfowl Trust at Slimbridge imported six birds from the US in 1948 that things got motoring. The trick, it turned out, was to allow the parent ducks to rear their own young. Soon there were *jamaicensis* families growing up there on the east of the Severn estuary.

Slimbridge policy was to clip the ducks' wings in order to prevent them escaping (the mink breeders' policy was to keep the mink in their cages, the crayfish farmers' policy was to keep the signal crayfish in their fisheries: living things are always liable to go wildly off-message). 1957 saw the first major breakout. In 1959 R. S. R. Fitter could add the ruddy duck to his list of once-captive species now seen "wandering full-winged about the countryside". In '71 the species collected its passport and in 1976, surveying the British history of the bird, Robert Hudson concluded that "it must be conceded that no harm appears to have been done to any native species or habitat, nor is there any danger of this essentially aquatic species becoming an agricultural pest. This is just as well because… Ruddy Ducks are successful and increasing, and all the signs are that they are here to stay."

They were and they weren't.

It's worth saying again: to birds, we might as well be weather. We might as well be a strong west-south-westerly wind, we might as well, to them, be nothing more than a change in the season—we're a geographical phenomenon; we just *happen*. Seeing the story of the ruddy duck in Britain as a bird might see it (flatly, starkly, without messy human-cultural context) it's clear that how the ruddy duck arrived here, how those first families were bred and born and how they dodged the wing-clippers in the Gloucestershire reedbeds, doesn't have any bearing at all on what they are now, in a given moment, snapshotted as a wild bird. They got here; they made it work. The mechanism is an irrelevance. We might as well watch an artic tern heaving-to over Noup Cliffs, its migration of twenty thousand miles at an end, and demand to know whether it rested at any point on an oilrig, or fed at any time on a trawler's discarded bycatch—and then, according to the answer, enter its name in column *a* or column *b*.

I can still remember how excited I was to see a drake ruddy duck—that bill!—on the flooded gravel pit where I used to go birdwatching as a boy of nine or ten. I suppose I saw it somewhat as another bird might: it was here, now, drifting just beyond the gravel spit, bright, rakish and excellent. The ruddy duck has the clean lines and innovative features of a design classic. I knew it well from my bird books. It somehow gave the impression of a bird that had been drawn first (perhaps by some late art deco artist) and only later translated into bone, flesh and feathers. The bird drifting out there on the lake might have been snipped from its page in my Kingfisher field guide. *Snap!*, said my brain.

Future British field guides won't feature the ruddy duck, except perhaps in some tucked-away 'rarities' subsection. In a way that's natural enough: I have a 1952 guide that includes the gyrfalcon and the flamingo, and a 1910 one that lists the great snipe and the pratincole (but doesn't even whisper of the mandarin duck or collared dove). They wouldn't be very good bird books if they didn't recognise change, because change is what wild things do; we'd all be stuck with something more like the oddest bird book on my shelf, Matthew Martyniuk's *Field Guide To Mesozoic Birds*, Huxley's Near Bird, Stocky Dragon, Hebei Thin Bird and all.

There are, however, different kinds of change.

About fifty ruddy duck generations (what for humans would amount to maybe fifteen hundred years) passed between our introduction of the ruddy duck to our islands and our decision to exterminate it. We began to shoot the ducks in 2005. It's true that there were, from a certain perspective, good ecological reasons for removing the ruddy ducks: they'd made it to Spain, and had begun interbreeding with the Spanish population of white-headed ducks. If they carried on carrying on in that way, the resultant hybrids (more ruddy than white-headed) would, over time, have replaced the white-headed duck entirely. No individual birds would have been displaced; rather, the two species would have in effect merged, creating, we can suppose, a new subspecies of ruddy duck. The pure-breed white-headed duck would—technically, in a genetic sense—have gone extinct (a PR problem in Spain, where the species is a poster-boy for wetland preservation).

We can argue over how much a duck cares about the integrity of its species. The point of the ruddy ducks' miserable story (it ends with their extinction—literal, actual, blood-in-the-water real—as a wild British bird) is not that we killed them all but that we felt that we *could* kill them all. That we had the right. That they were in some sense ours.

If the accidental Scilly bufflehead of 1920 had, by chance, run into a similarly storm-driven drake bufflehead on a Tresco lakeside, and they had bred, and their ducklings had bred, and so on—and if, decades later, these Scilly buffleheads (now, we can suppose, spread across the wetlands of the south-west, a familiar sight on the Exe and the Otter) had begun to interbreed with, say, British goldeneye, to the point where the goldeneye's genetic line faced subsumption—would we then, like over-protective fathers, have reached for our shotguns?

Perhaps, after all, we would. Perhaps it's not all about notions of 'natural' and 'unnatural'; notions of 'British' and 'foreign' are at play here, too, and such is the intervolution of all these ideas that they may be impossible to pick apart. In any case, we're still talking about column *a* and column *b*, about origin, backstory, as a metric of value—we're talking about good immigrants and bad immigrants, and we're visiting the sins of the fathers (captivity; escape; ferality; freedom) upon the children, even unto the fiftieth generation.

If we have made mistakes—Eugene Schieffelin wouldn't have called them mistakes, but then Eugene Schieffelin was a lunatic, wasn't he?—then it's right that we should admit to them, and desirable that we should learn from them; it doesn't, though, give us a free hand to try to claw back the consequences. Mistakes can't be unmade. Which brings us to *let's try that again*.

They live a flickering greyscale afterlife on YouTube: sound-tracked by piano ballads, captioned with user comments (*it sucks that we killed off God's creation of species that was suppose to roam the earth; humans are vermin on the earth; I love how people are acting like animals only started going extinct when humans came around; quite depressing!*). These are the twentieth-century extinctions. Here's the Laysan crake of Hawaii, extinct since

1944, loping in undercranked slo-mo across a landscape of sand and rock; here's the last thylacine, the Tasmanian tiger, fretting in its enclosure at Hobart Zoo, dead by 1933; here, bobbing and leaping at lek on a Massachusetts heath, are heath hens, all gone by 1932.

Leave YouTube behind, search for *revive restore* in a new tab.

"De-extinction expands ecological restoration capabilities", says the genetics project's website. "It is perhaps the ultimate form of genetic rescue."

We can rebuild him, as the intro voiceover used to say on 'The Six Million Dollar Man'. *We have the technology.*

The last heath hen was nicknamed 'Booming Ben'. He lived on a reserve on Martha's Vineyard, south of Cape Cod, alone, genetically wrung-out, sounding his resonant mating-call each spring, even though there were no female heath hens left to hear it. "The bird presented a pathetic figure as it stood out there all alone", wrote Bowdoin College professor Alfred O. Gross, "without any companions save the crows that had come to share the food intended for the heath hen". He died in March, 1932—five years after the last of the others.

Heath hens, *Tympanuchus cupido cupido*, were a portly grouse species that occupied the 'barrens' of the US eastern seaboard: prior to the nineteenth century, they were extremely common—like more than a few other now-extinct species, they were considered a good dinner for a poor man, easy to catch and okay to eat. The birds relied on grassland habitat that was kept close-cropped by natural grassfires. European colonists suppressed the fires, and let taller, thicker vegetation take hold on the barrens. Coupled with the regular harvest of hens for the pot, it was enough to wipe the heath hen from the US mainland—by the 1870s only a remnant population remained, out on the salt-washed sandplains of the Vineyard. Here they were protected and cared for, after a fashion: the islanders maintained a hen-friendly habitat, but their suppression of natural fires allowed a build-up of combustible material. When, in May 1916, a fire *did* break out, it ripped through and ravaged the heath hen breeding grounds, stripping a population of around two thousand down to just a hundred and fifty, with an unsustainable preponderance of males. A genetic bottleneck strangled the heath hen. It stumbled on as a species, inbred and debilitated, for another eighteen years, then, in the ailing form of Booming Ben, died off.

Bringing it back through genetic wizardry would perhaps be the last word in "let's try that again" introductions.

We call it 'de-extinction' but it's no such thing. What's done can't be undone. It's true that we can reinvent or reimagine the heath hen (or the Laysan crake or the passenger pigeon or the dodo, why not), we can make some things that look and act like those birds, but we can't reverse the innumerable deaths that added up to those extinctions in the first place, we can't simply scroll the progress bar backwards like we can on those YouTube videos—we can't de-extinguish these species, not really, any more than my waking up in the morning undoes the fact that I fell asleep the night before. The world moves on regardless, and every living thing is locked into that onward motion.

I think a bird's being extends beyond its outstretched wing-tips; its identity is knotted up in its habitat, in the world that has shaped it, and continues to shape it. Birds change, we change, the world changes. There really are no reintroductions. Places might go by the same old names but they're new, always new, always different (perhaps subtly, perhaps wildly, but different).

If we do press ahead with so-called 'de-extinction'—and we've done it already, momentarily, in the case of the extinct Pyrenean ibex, which we cloned in 2009, only for the new ibex to die just after birth—then it'll be an introduction much like many others. The only difference will be that the introduced birds will be delivered by a lab and a surrogate (a farmyard chicken in the case of the heath hen), and not by crate or cage from Norway or Germany or Spain, which is the way we've done it before.

London's last red kite nest, in Gray's Inn Gardens, was pulled down in 1777. Now these birds are seen winnowing their forked tails and browsing for roadkill over Enfield and Southall, Richmond and Wandsworth, Feltham and Putney, Sidcup and Pinner, Bexleyheath and Forest Hill. We sent them away—drove them, through persecution and habitat destruction, into a final redoubt in deep mid-Wales—and brought them back. But to say that we reintroduced them to south-east England is to suggest that the London of today is the London of 1777.

It's true that it bears the same name. It's true that certain old stones still stand where they did before—perhaps certain old trees, too, and certain old lanes and holloways still follow the same old tracks. But it's a different place. Imagine that one of those kites of Gray's Inn, fledged in the reign of George III, fell into a sleep as it drifted with the wind north from High Holborn, over the fallow grassland of Lamb's Conduit Fields, beyond the city turnpikes; imagine it fell into a sleep of two hundred and thirty years or so, and awoke today, blinking in the particulate haze of an Airbus contrail, buffeted by bywinds bent by the Triton Building and Euston Tower, seeing suddenly, below, through a dull filter of reeking exhaust gas, endless acres of brick and slate, asphalt and wrought iron, indecipherable patterns of railway and road—it seems improbable that the kite would think, *Ah: this is London.*

If the kite flexed its rudder-like tail to tilt southward, it would pass above what seemed a city, but was stripped of the appetising city smells of horseshit and slaughterhouse (perhaps the kite would instead pick up, amid the chemical pongs, a complicated new savour: cooking meat, unfamiliar spices, decomposing food-waste). To the north, it would find *more* city: the old cricketfields of Lamb's Conduit long built over, the hedgerows grubbed up, some rats about the place but not much more, not half so many songbirds as it remembered; only a little green to be seen amid the greyscale, clipped and corralled into rectangles (what we call Regent's Square Gardens, and Brill Place, and Grimaldi Park).

There would be much for the red kite to enjoy here—but this would not be the London the kite left behind. It wouldn't be an old friend, not seen in years, a little more grey and stooped, dog-eared, marked by time, but still *the same person underneath* —there'd be no 'underneath', from a kite's eye view, there'd be only what's there, now, caught in the kite's raking binocular vision: there'd be a new place, where—judging by the sit of the stars and the lie of the land—that other place used to be.

Anyway, all this supposes that the kites are the same, too—

that the kites we drove away in the eighteenth century are the same kites we installed in Yorkshire and the Chilterns two-and-a-bit centuries later. But of course those were new birds, starting from scratch. We're not privy to the conversations of birds, but did kites maintain an oral history of old London or old Leeds, a folk-memory of Tudor middens or early-modern abattoir runoff, did they somehow keep alive an atavistic imagining of the human city, a place of open sewers, black rats, horsemeat and poultry-yards, pass it in story or song from bird to bird across eighty generations? It seems more likely that that slate was wiped clean long ago—that the kites would never think "this has changed", but only "this is new".

The introduction project is a by-product of extinction, which is a very human idea. Most often—except where the likes of Revive Restore enter the fray, marshalling swabs and petri dishes, measuring out their reams of genetic code like lengths of tickertape—it has to do with *local* extinction, which is doubly human: it takes a human's perspective, first to lump all these birds (all the heath hens, or all the great auks, or all the red kites) together as a 'species', and second to consider it significant that species *x* does or doesn't exist within or without a certain ragged outline on a map. When I say, by the way, that these things are human concerns, as things that wouldn't mean much to the birds whose shuttling about seems so important to us, it isn't at all to demean them; our personal perspectives are at the heart of who we are, and their importance isn't diminished when we point out that they have limits, that there are other perspectives, other ways of looking, thinking, valuing.

Extinction is something we frame as the saddest story of all. We set the lonely deaths of 'Booming Ben' and Martha the passenger pigeon in the context of a general dwindling, a species-wide fade from history, and we see in these last birds an apotheosis of loneliness. In 1954 Fred Bodsworth published the novel *The Last Of The Curlews*—really a mix of novel and non-fiction—which dramatised the last lonely migrations of the last-ever eskimo curlew ("The tundra call was irresistible.

He flew again and called once more. Then he leveled off, the rising sun glinted pinkly on his feathers, and he headed north in silence, alone"). You can hear violins rising on the soundtrack as you read but in fact a good deal of the pathos in the book derives from the unnamed curlew's obliviousness to his species' fate—the painful contrast between what the curlew 'knows' ("the territory must be held in readiness for the female his instinct told him soon would come": that's the last line) and what we know (that there is no female, not there in the tundra, not anywhere on this earth).

If we thought differently about these things we might even find something cheering in Bodsworth's characterisation—sure, this is the last curlew, but see how *hopeful* he still is—but a converse and more valuable rethinking might nudge us to reflect not on the birds' indifference to extinction but on the fact that *no* bird is indifferent to death.

A starling's congeners might blot out the sun but the starling would still rather not, thanks very much, be picked off at the fringe of its flock by a late-hunting peregrine. Martha the pigeon died alone in an Ohio zoo but it's hard to believe she would sooner have been shot out of the sky by an orchardkeeper's flintlock during the passenger pigeon's boomtime a hundred years before. Josef Stalin is supposed to have said that one death is a tragedy, a million deaths a statistic. We don't think like that where birds are concerned. It's sometimes only once a million birds lie dead that we pay any attention at all.

Mark Cocker has written of the knowledgeable naturalist living "suspended in a landscape of losses". He calls extinction a drama that enables "anyone... to understand the feelings of sadness and the urgent motives for action". Extinction is emotionally accessible, not hard to get a handle on, compared with the subtle gradations of decline, the nuances that to one who knows the language signal a biodiversity slump or ecosystem under stress.

Intellectually, too, extinction is pretty easy: once they were here—these moa, these curlews, these Hawai'ian songbirds, these hen harriers—and now they aren't. Easier, certainly, than processing census data that maps the trajectories over several years of a few dozen different species, with all the blips, mysteries, switchbacks and subtleties that that might encode. So we use extinction as a crude way of keeping score. How are we getting on? Not well. Really, not well at all.

But would we be doing any better if we had a few dozen po'o-uli—extinct since the mid-00s, we think—still clinging on among the dry myrtles of Maui, a relict population of Bachman's warblers (since the 1980s) in some derelict Louisiana canebrake, a last stand of imperial woodpeckers (since the '50s) high in the wooded highlands of Mexico—but there were only a handful of lapwing pairs left in Eurasia's dwindling wetland, global sparrow populations were shrunk to a genetically impoverished rump scraping a living in the rundown suburbs, and we had to trek to the Siberian steppe to watch the last skydances of breeding hen harriers, to the forested massifs of central Europe to hear, if we're lucky, the gentle vibrato of the turtle dove? How about if we had a Noah's ark's worth of birds—two of each, everything in moderation? There are all sorts of puzzling questions here about biodiversity (what if we have trillions of birds, but here's the catch, *they're all starlings*), and really no obvious right answers, but it can't hurt to acknowledge that extinction means more to us than it does to the birds, and that death—everyday death, death by cold, by cat, by sparrowhawk, by hunger, by disease—means more to the birds than it does to us.

4. *Home*

At San Sebastián, which the Basques call Donostía, I saw a black redstart on the wet black rocks that keep the sea from the coast road. It was snaffling insects beneath the noses of three ranks of picnicking spectators. This was the Kontxako Bandera: a boat race, staged here each September. Thirteen colossal Basque oarsmen per flat-bottomed *trainera*, hauling out and back across the Bay of the Concha. The race is steeped—or perhaps salt-cured—in the maritime history of Atlantic Spain; it's a fisherman's race, of boats first built to hurry sardines and anchovies from trawler to market. Thousands of people—local people, fans from all along the ragged length of the coast, clueless tourists like me—assemble to watch. They have sandwiches and salt cod, bottles of Coke, red wine, sharp local cider. Ranged along the arms of the bay that cup the sea, they cheer their boats out and cheer them back in again. It's physical, visceral, and deeply political (*everything* that's Basque is deeply political), and consciously historic—it's all so brightly and busily *human*.

The black redstart was distinguished by its indifference. It wasn't here to hustle for crumbs of baguette or sugary *ocho*. It didn't want anything from us. For all it cared, we might as well not have been there. This is the default policy of the black redstart.

In Britain it's an urban bird, a city bird (indeed a City bird, the only real songster of EC1). Unlike pigeons, jackdaws, starlings and sparrows, it doesn't really have a relationship with us. That is, it's not here for the food, it's here for the infrastructure.

What is a city? Forget what we made it for. What is it now? In one place it's a sea of cliff-faces, row on row, stark and weirdly lit but high and hard and safe, pocked with inviting recesses. It's sometimes said that city buildings *mimic* cliffs. That's not right—they *are* cliffs, as far as birds are concerned. If it does what a cliff does it's a cliff. What *we* call it is by the bye.

The cliffs I know best are those on the North Sea coast of Yorkshire. They're part of a layer of chalk, half a kilometre thick, that rained out of the seawater that covered the land in the late Cretaceous period, perhaps seventy million years ago. A block of chalk is a bonehouse, really, an ancient ossuary. What's now white rock was once *calcareous ooze*, a sea-bottom sludge of fossilised micro-skeletons: phytoplankton, foraminifera, ostracods, molluscs—all the microscopic-scale life of the prehistoric oceans (a vegan climber I know says he declines to climb chalk cliffs for this reason; I think he's joking). The Yorkshire chalk of Flamborough and Bempton heaved up out of the sea between perhaps sixty and twenty million years ago. Thomas Henry Huxley wrote in 1868 that "a great chapter of the history of the world is written in the chalk", and this is true: chalk is a chronicle of countless non-human generations, not only of those minuscule sea-things but, a few chapters further on, of birds, too.

It's not as though they were waiting for the cliffs to rear above the North Sea waves. Back when these were not cliffs but chalk reefs, barnacled and green, barely cresting the water, the forebears of cormorants would have perched on their tops, the forebears of gannets would have plunged into the rich surrounding waters to feed on the forebears of sardines; in bird terms, this would have been a working landscape, as, to birds, all landscapes are. Whatever forms a landscape takes, the birds' response—the way birds deal with it—will be spontaneous, *ad hoc*, improvised on the wing.

When the Flamborough chalk began its slow rise from the sea floor the birds that in the modern age dominate its guano-whitened terraces were not yet what they are today. Taking the long view, the evolutionary view, they were finding their form, taking shape, figuring out how best to fit (taking the long view, birds are *always* doing that). In the short view, the remote ancestors of the auks—the guillemots, razorbills and puffins—were busy getting by, urgently feeding and breeding and being not-quite-auks within seabird communities strewn across the oceans.

By about fifty million years ago, the birds' dispersal had enabled a growing-apart, an incipient speciation: the puffins took an evolutionary turn away from the razorbills and guille-mots, slowly, of course, in fact invisibly, and knowing nothing of it themselves—a change of a kind with the rising of the chalk, no less gradual, no less infinitesimal in its increments, but at the same time no less real (it's easy to find yourself thinking of geological time as though it's a metaphor or a thought experi-ment) and, in retrospect, hardly less monumental.

Today we have towering cliffs at Flamborough and Bempton, and those three distinct auk species breed in huge numbers on the ancient chalk (the razorbill is huskier, darker, and has a worldlier look than the guillemot; the burrow-nesting puffin, a less close cousin, strays further from the guillemot's no-frills auk template, with its gaudy orange feet and summer party beak). Bempton, in particular, is a seabird city, and a port city at that, a place of visitations and intermixings as well as home-comings, as raffishly vibrant and cosmopolitan as a Shanghai, a Liverpool, a Cadiz, a Naples—a throng of interconnected lives, noisy, thrilling, stinking (seabird shit in these quantities smells evocatively of fishpaste and ammonia). The auk populations here jockey for elbowroom with colonies of yawping kittiwakes, with gannets, mad-eyed and big as geese, with the odd serene fulmar, tube-nosed and stiff-winged, with rock doves, peregrines and interloping herring gulls, the whole lot at once both genetically *made* for this kind of life on the edge and making it up as they go along.

By 'rock dove' I perhaps mean 'pigeon'. Seen in freeze-frame—which is how, in evolutionary terms, we see everything, snapshotted with an exposure of mere, insignificant centuries —these birds are in an in-between place (whereas, as they see themselves, they're just *there*, wherever 'there' is, at home as they'll ever be). *Columba livia*, double-identitied, both the rock dove of weatherbeaten sea-cliffs and the ne'er-do-well feral pigeon of the city square, in some ways tells us a story about birds and their adaptability—but it also tells us something important about landscapes: about what birds see, and what we see, and about the indifference of birds to where we think they ought to be.

There's no place in this book for what, exactly, thousands of years of domestication did to the wild pigeon. There's no room for the Carrier, the Dragoon, the Barb, the Antwerp, the Pouter, the Jacobean or the Tumbler (all varieties of 'fancy pigeon', carved by selective breeding from the raw material of the rock dove much as the greyhound, pug and beagle were carved from the wolf)—but we can talk about what happened when the rock dove awoke, so to speak, from its domestication. In effect it was a sudden relocation: the rock dove snatched from its cliffside retreat, run through a sort of factory or mill (tweaked, tinkered with, souped up, remodelled) and then—not much different, after all, in the main—let go. *These are your cliffs now*, we might have said, gesturing, perhaps, at kippered mill-chimneys, roof-tops, high-rises, clocktowers, cathedral spires, skyscrapers. Cocking its head, beadily eyeballing the towering sandstone or brick or steel or concrete, the rock dove might have said: *all right*.

The 'feral' pigeon isn't really feral; to me, it's wild. These are wild rock doves, and the fact that the world has shifted beneath their feet—that they find themselves flocking under flyovers or on window ledges rather than on outcropping Skye gneiss or St Kilda granite—doesn't alter that. The starling, the nineteenth century nature writer William Henry Hudson wrote, builds in an urban niche "just as he does in a hole in a tree in a forest, or a hole in the rock on some sea-cliff, where instead of men and women he has puffins, guillemots, and gannets for neighbours. The roar of the sea or the jarring noises of human traffic and industry—it is all one to the starling." So it was with the dove *Columba livia*. These birds saw a new kind of cliff rise from the earth, understood it for what it was, and, disregarding the chimney smoke as they'd disregarded sea-spray, braving cats and cars as they'd braved skuas and peregrines, made their homes in it.

The rising of our human cliffs was far faster than the uplifting of the Flamborough chalk. It was all over in an eyeblink, though to us it seems a spasmodic, stammering process. Our first eminences were not cliffs so much as hills, heaps, broad-bottomed and tapered, pyramids, mausoleums, mosques, minsters; only later did we start to make something more like a sea-stack, to make our own precipitous and free-standing columnar cliffs, not winnowed from mineral as stacks are by the waves and wind but scraped up out of the earth and piled, balanced, cantilevered impossibly into skyscrapers, monuments and vanity towers. It took us, by our yardstick, a lot of generations, but it was nothing compared with the generations of chalk. Anyway, up they leapt, these human cliffs, and there—pretty much right away, no doubt—were birds.

The pigeons that have roosted on the flanks of Giza's Great Pyramid for millennia wouldn't have waited till it was finished: picture them, as the sun sets in a dark-rose sky behind Khufu's great building site, assembling on the great granite terraces, murmuring, throat-puffing, jockeying for place, whitening the undressed stone with their shit. We don't know if the lighthouse at Pharos was draped with the weed of a kittiwake nest (or what birds took to its ruins to roost after the earthquake of 956); we don't know whether yellow-legged gulls patrolled the roofs of the mausoleum at Halicarnassus or if bee-eaters perched and snatched at hornets dodging among the marble columns of Ephesus—but we do know that the birds' view of these places would have been free of the human filters of history and status, beauty and meaning.

It's not all about us, might be the message. We might have built these things (though much of the work was done before we got here: we didn't forge marble from limestone, or mulch silicates into workable clay, or alchemise iron ore), but once they were there, once they were in the world, we were sharing them, like it or not. Birds are territorial with members of their own species but where we're concerned they don't tend to recognise 'ours' and 'theirs'; instead they work with 'can' and 'can't'. I can roost here. I can nest here. I can live here.

And these are not temporary lodgings, city dosshouses, for the birds. The colony of kittiwakes on the Tyne Bridge in Newcastle has been in place since the early 'sixties, and only grows larger and more durable. In September 1666, with the City of London in flames, Samuel Pepys noted that "the poor pigeons... were loth to leave their houses, but hovered about the windows and balconies, till they some of them burned their wings and fell down". The ornithologist Collingwood Ingram, stationed in St-André during the First World War, was impressed by the site fealty of the house sparrows who hung around bombed-out towns "in which every house has lain, for a year or more, a mere heap of rubble and bricks". These places we once built are now so much more than we ever meant them to be.

"How much would be lost to the sculptured west front of Wells Cathedral, the soaring spire of Salisbury, the noble roof and towers of York Minster and of Canterbury, if the jackdaws were not there!" declared W. H. Hudson. "It is a pity that, before consenting to rebuild St Paul's Cathedral, Sir Christopher Wren did not make the perpetual maintenance of a colony of jackdaws a condition. And if he had bargained with posterity for a pair or two of peregrine falcons and kestrels, his glory at the present time would have been greater." But I don't like to think of jackdaws and kestrels this way—to look at them with the eye of an interior decorator, thinking *now what this place really needs...*

There's a view of the world in which the non-human parts amount to not much more than an enthusiast's rose-garden or a collector's display case. Sometimes we want to curate more than we want to conserve, because where's the fun in stepping back, what's exciting about being hands-off, what's the point if it doesn't wind up how we want it, why should we bother if we won't get the credit?

It's true that sometimes wild things can use a hand (nestbox, peanut feeder, birdbath) but these kinds of interventions can come with strings attached. We have a lurking sense, I think, of ownership, of a part-share in the birds' lives; an insistent idea that we're allowing the birds—provisionally, on condition of decent behaviour—into 'our' sphere, accommodating them, ushering them graciously (fatball, sir? Nijer seed, madam?) into our human worldview.

Sure, they'll share our physical space, but they'll keep their own worldview, thanks. They'll continue to move around a shifting world without being bothered why it's shifting—they'll carry on playing the smart game, working the angles, keeping out an eye for the main chance, occupying, as always, their *own* sphere.

Sometimes we talk about 'wild' and 'tame' as though these are opposites, extremes on a spectrum. From a bird's perspective, though, they're both just matters of practical policy.

That pigeon scrabbling up tourists' birdseed from the city paving, or that chaffinch hunting cake-crumbs on a café patio, or that robin taking leatherjackets from a gardener's hand—these are wild birds being wild; that is, doing what the heck they like, pursuing profitable opportunities, taking the calculated risks they have to take to get the things they need (they are, in the jargon of self-help, *living their best lives*).

It's not a great leap from fancifully decking out your cathedral with jackdaws to, let's say, caging a bullfinch to sing in your drawing-room; both come from thinking of birds as an accessory, a complement to the things we think are human. Better, perhaps, to embrace the birds' indifference. To try to see that 'ours' is also 'theirs'. To watch kestrels hunt in the cathedral cloister and think not how wonderfully they set off the architecture but, rather, how wonderful it is that this thing we call 'architecture' has within it a whole other meaning, a whole alternative reality, a whole *bunch* of alternative realities: the kestrels' reality, the pigeons' or sparrows' or herring gulls' reality, realities of shelter, airflow, altitude, prey, peace—the birds' reality.

Termites don't draw up blueprints or construct interactive 3-D simulations. They build, without apparently thinking very much about it, what needs building. The gluey word 'stigmergy' describes the termites' motivation as they construct their towers or 'termitaria': it means *incitement to work*, where the incitement is not (of course) money or status or the terms of an employment contract but only the need for the work to be done. Insect builders don't communicate their building plans to each other directly but instead do it indirectly, via the structure of the building itself: if task *a* has been done, then we must do task *b*. So it goes on, until something extraordinary has been accomplished: a termitarium four years in the building might tower, brick-red and clay-rich, more than five metres above the savannah.

The termites don't build the same way we do, but they've been in the skyscraper business for far longer than we have. One petrified New Mexico termitarium complex might be 155 million years old. A non-fossil mound in the Congo basin dates back at least two millennia. We only threw up the *New York World* building in 1894, the Singer building in 1909, the Sears Tower in

1998, the Taipei 101 and the Burj Khalifa in the last twenty years (for the record, scaling up in proportion, a termite mound made by human-sized termites would be as tall as three Burj Khalifas stacked one on another, and only condors and vultures would circle its cloud-kissing spire).

There's a lot of history between buildings—whoever builds them—and birds.

Puffbirds don't care how termites build termite mounds any more than black redstarts care how we built Dungeness B. The puffbird sees a termitarium for what it is. And not just puffbirds but trogons, peach-fronted parakeets, yellow-faced parrots, American kestrels, ferruginous pygmy-owls, Toco toucans, brown-chested martins, Chopi blackbirds and chestnut-eared aracaris—all, as they crisscross the plains of South America, have regarded the tall towers and long shadows of the termite cities and seen not the workings of a swarming superorganism but only a convenient place to roost, or nest; not someone else's home, but a place to make their own.

In Brazil, forty-five different bird species have been seen to make homes in the baked-clay megalopolises of the termites. Some birds—woodpeckers, parrots, puffbirds—dig out their own niches in the fabric of the mound; many, though, occupy holes or nooks previously excavated by others (indifferent, again, to any idea of *purpose* in the structure, seeing a hole as only a hole and no more as a woodpecker's nest than as a termite high-rise). Many of these species would more usually resort to a cavity in a tree-trunk to lay eggs and raise young, but on the wide-open plains of South America a tree is not always available when one is required, and a warm nook in a tall termitarium is a good plan 'b'. It will offer security, and what scientists call a *propitious microclimate* (one of the main 'jobs' of the termitarium, from the termites' point of view, is to stabilise the internal temperature, balancing—in some startlingly complex ways involving thermal mass and convective flow—the fluctuating temperatures of tropical night and day).

And even if you don't require a home, but only, for the time being, a place to stand, the termitaria are again your friend: the southern caracara and the burrowing owl use termite mounds as lookouts, watchtowers from which they scan the plains for prey; channel-billed toucans and swallowtail kites use them as take-off points from which to launch twisting mid-air assaults on winged insects (including termites); the male Campo miner—a chat-like bird of sunburnt South American grassland—will strut atop a termitarium to perform its madcap flap-and-jabber spring displays; the male red-legged seriema, too, uses the termites' spire for display, in his case to deliver a strange, squealing laugh of a song (to which the female replies in kind, as though the two seriemas find one another an absolute hoot). Tall termite mounds are routinely seen to be streaked with these birds' white guano.

Analogues are not hard to find.

Human cities, too, can furnish a propitious microclimate. Cities are heat islands, (relatively) small pockets of secret warmth in the wide, dark countryside. The effect is especially notable at night: fractional differentials in diurnal temperature can correspond to two or three degrees at night-time, the kind of marginal gain that can be life-or-death for small birds. Urban Barcelona has an overnight low of around 2.9 degrees higher than the surrounding countryside, and the Catalan starlings know it: for many decades their murmurations have billowed over the Plaça Catalunya at nightfall (though their numbers are not what they were). Central London in the dusk gradually fills up with starlings flying in from the suburbs, inverting commuter convention by treating the inner city as a dormitory. Winter pied wagtails—once known for bedding down amid tomato-plants and sacks of compost in gardeners' greenhouses—also hungrily hunt out those stray extra degrees of warmth, staking out roosts in Carlisle and Cairo, Leicester and Sbeitla, Osnabruck, Milan, Beirut, Hong Kong and Edinburgh. Overlay the distribution patterns of these roosting birds on to a city map and see how the shapes of the roosts conform to the urban isotherms, the patterns of the city's exhaled warmth: vents, flues, cooling towers, outflows.

And there's security in nest-holes here as much as in the nest-holes clawed out of warm and termite-mined Cerrado clay. A nook among the Gothic complications of a medieval cathedral tower. A flaw in a gutter or a gap where a rooftile used to be. A window ledge seven storeys above the Chicago Loop. A hole in the hand of the Duke of Wellington's statue at the Royal Exchange. An angle of girders on a smoke-blacked iron bridge. A hollow pipe suspending a streetlight over a Manhattan intersection. Cities are made of things, crammed with things, often seeming so busy, so *full*, but they are made, too, of spaces between things, of nooks, gaps, recesses, cracks, ginnels, alleyways, openings (to a consciousness operating at songbird-scale, one hundredth of our size, six hundredth of our weight, cities must seem almost hollow). These are the places where the birds live.

We construct human realities around the things we make, the things we build. We give them names and identities that are bound up with what they used to be, or what we wish them to be, or what we think they're for. Birds see a different reality: flatter, sharper-edged, locked into the present moment: what is this now, what is it good for *now*?

The southern caracara—goshawk-sized, pale-cheeked, a mantle of fine barring like lace or chainmail about its shoulders, a black bed-head crest—has no thought of the termites teeming beneath its feet when it grips the turret of a termitarium the better to survey its territory; just the same, the red-tailed hawk balanced on a Brooklyn tv aerial to watch for pigeons doesn't care much about the people down below watching *Sunday Night Football* or *The Big Bang Theory*, doesn't care about the invisible ripple of the tv signal or the electrical micro-currents zipping through the aluminium array—it's just a place to do what the hawk needs to do.

The Cerrado of South America is one kind of savanna. London is another. It's true that there are no herds of wildebeest or buffalo there—only one large mammal species makes great migrations across London's plains—but the definition applies, nevertheless. Cities are, in botanical terms, open spaces, usually without much tree cover; vegetation is fragmented and tends to be low-growing (you get more in the way of shrubs and weeds than of forest canopy). Vegetation is central to the way birds characterise a place. Characterising the city—any city—in this way is another step towards seeing 'our' spaces as the birds see them.

"The robin", the great naturalist Max Nicholson wrote in his 1951 book *Birds & Men*, "views the town as a kind of forest heavily cut up and at times hopelessly swamped by sterile and inhospitable buildings, and follows the tapering fingers or isolated splashes of trees and bushes as far inwards towards the town centre as considerations of cover and food supply permit. The black redstart views a town as a series of artificial ravines, which may or may not offer suitable precipices for breeding near enough suitable foraging patches on which insects and so forth can be picked up in adequate quantity without undue interruption by people, cats, dogs and rival species of birds."

We're back to the black redstart. It's significant that the human concept 'finished' doesn't mean anything to birds. Nor does the concept of 'derelict'. The black redstart has no real use either for us—it doesn't want our birdseed or our refuse, but only the insects which cohabit with both us and it—or for our ideas about what is and isn't a useful building.

Certainly it will make good use of those buildings that we consider finished and functioning: philosophically, the black redstart would buy into the ethos of Manhattan's skyscraper moguls in the first decades of the twentieth century—it's the 'really high' buildings that the black redstart is interested in, Nicholson wrote, and his list of urban nest sites is extraordinarily evocative: Wembley's Palace of Engineering, Westminster Abbey, Cambridge University, Croydon Airport, Woolwich Arsenal (not to mention Altenberg Cathedral and the boulders of the polar-bear enclosure at Cologne Zoo). So it's true that the black redstart wants us to construct these tall, stark places, but it also wants us to leave at least some of them alone ("build and bugger off" might be its principle). In the mid-twentieth century we could hardly have done more to meet the redstarts' brief.

It's a bit of a myth that these birds' colonisation of London was a consequence of the Blitz—that first Wembley pair set up home in 1926 at the latest, and the species' steady infiltration of our urban spaces was part of a general drift north-west in the European population—but the Luftwaffe's slapdash urban clearances of 1940-41 certainly didn't harm the habitat, from a black redstart's point of view. The Germans' bombs wrought a haphazard sort of destruction: where one building was flattened, its neighbour might have been left standing, and so the black redstarts were able to enact a strategy we might characterise as "breed on the building, feed on the bombsite". The birds, in doing this, in moving to occupy this world of iron and slate and soot-blacked brick, and in pursuing insect-life among the groundsel and rosebay willowherb ('bombweed') of the emptied lots, weren't being resourceful, exactly; they saw these habitats of cliff and scrub flower unexpectedly in the heart of London and they moved in, simply because they could. Once again they saw these places for what they were. Just because for us to see buildings and bombsites as places for birds we have to squint and tilt our heads to one side, it doesn't mean that it's not plainly evident from a black redstart's perspective.

It's a long time since birds were first drawn to the strange gravity of human towns.

We had no skyscrapers then, no pyramids, only roundhouses of wattle-and-daub, built on stone, built to endure, but still, no rock dove's idea of a secure nesting-place, no peregrine's idea of a vantage-point. But they came anyway. At Hallan Çemi, as the place is now called, we lived for perhaps three centuries, and the birds were there too.

Hallan Çemi in south-eastern Turkey was first occupied by people in the early Holocene, around 11,700 years ago. Today there are no people there and no birds: Hallan Çemi is underwater, flooded by the waters of the Batman River where they pool behind the dam built by Turkey in the nineteen-nineties. Before then it was a quiet place in the semi-arid desert of Anatolia. But those three hundred years or so of neolithic occupation left marks, long-lasting souvenirs of a civilisation; like all relics, these souvenirs tell stories.

The old bones of long-dead birds might tell human stories with birds in them or bird stories with humans in them, depending on your point of view. Digging around in the early nineties—gatecrashing preliminary excavation for the reservoir—archaeologists found dozens of birds at Hallan Çemi; Smithsonian archaeo-ornithologist Megan Spitzer, sifting the thousand-plus bones unearthed at the site, identified fifty-one taxa spread across twenty families and thirteen orders of birds (orders are things like Accipitriformes, most diurnal birds of prey; families are things like Cathartidae, the vultures and condors). There are birds here that can tell us about how these neolithic Anatolians lived, hunted, ate and conducted ritual, but there are also birds that speak to us—across a distance, remember, of almost twelve thousand years—about what they saw, as this entirely new thing, this first idea of a human town, sprouted from the sands.

Elephant-sized ground sloths still lumbered across the grassland of South America at this point. The glaciers were not long gone. Humans were not yet farmers (though we may, in some places, have been shepherds and goatherds). Many birds now long-extinct still had a good few centuries left on the clock: Dow's puffin on the Channel Islands, the Cuban poorwill in the Caribbean, the asphalt stork of California's La Brea tarpits.

Hallan Çemi was a junction town, a settlement at the meeting-point of six fertile ecozones: grassland, mountain, rocky open country, wooded steppe, woodland, and wetland. It's where you'd choose to live if you really needed to kill things. We can imagine a black vulture watching our arrival with interest from the top of a tall helix of rising air—our getting there, and then *staying there*. We can try to see ourselves caught in the glaring yellow eye of a stone curlew, paused in mid-run across the sparse grass to watch us as we dig trenchwork, heave stones, fetch water, shovel clay.

Birds get used to things. They, too, are prey to shifting baseline syndrome: a new normal every moment, the world overhauled, the odds recalculated. Edwardian photographers clung to the idea that unfamiliarity was a panic trigger for birds, and so they crammed themselves and their unwieldy cameras inside stuffed cows and mimetic sheep, plywood boulders and mocked-up hayricks, but, as the writer John Bevis has pointed out, "birds have no such reflex. What does arouse suspicion and alarm is sights and sounds that are abrupt or indicative of preda-tion." They would have noted, these birds of neolithic Anatolia, our forward-facing predators' eyes, perhaps our meat-eaters' mouths, perhaps something rangy and lupine in the way we moved, carried ourselves, took in our surroundings. But there were other things of interest to see. There might be prizes here, too. Those rolling cost-benefit estimates would have again ratcheted and refreshed, creating new landscapes of risk and reward.

These were, by and large, birds whose patterns still wheel across the earth: grey partridge, great bustard, quail, wigeon, shelduck, pochard, griffon vulture, peregrine, long-eared owl, crane, heron, coot, lapwing, moorhen—there would be few avian mysteries for the time-traveller set down in neolithic Hallan Çemi with a pair of binoculars and the *Peterson Guide to the Birds of Britain and Europe*. They were meeting us, then, in the infancy of our civilisation. They learned quickly enough that we were hunters (as our eyes and teeth had promised): a reading of the bones tells us that we went most hungrily after the partridge and the meaty great bustard—a leggy metre tall, and accustomed, in those days, to gather on the plains in herds of thousands—but that we weren't especially choosy about birdmeat; we guess that most of the birds whose bones we found at Hallan Çemi were caught in the hills, or the woods, or the wetlands, and came only posthumously to the town.

But there was surely more to our transactions than the hunt. There was the waste. There always is.

Some species would have been drawn into Hallan Çemi by the waste itself. A vulture will always find more meat on a bone than a human can. Canny crows—jackdaws, magpies—would soon have clocked the town as a place of turbulent and profitable bustle, of butchery, cookery, the preparation of gathered grains and plants, of flyblown latrines, of burial. These species might have formed the first wave, the first layer of the birds' engagement with an urban habitat. A second layer would have observed rats and mice scampering over the vultures' prints in the dirt, through the sand scuffed up by the ruckus of crows picking at the butcher's tools, and would have retooled their tactics accordingly—by night the moonshadow of hunting eagle owls (six feet, wingtip to wingtip) would have passed over the roundhouses. We can't know for sure how each bird's bones wound up in the Hallan Çemi soil. These birds, too, may have come to the town in a hunter's bag, but there's a good likelihood that they were there on their own initiative—that their deaths at the hands of our ancestors were a result not of a hunt but of human opportunism. These crows, vultures, owls and raptors might have been what ecologists call "targets of opportunity", scavengers scavenged, gamblers scalped. A jackdaw brained by slingshot as it loiters hopefully where a sheep is being skinned. An owl snatched or speared while bent over a pinned rat.

The movements of bird populations around an emerging town might be likened to a hand reaching into a trap, seeking hesitantly to grab the bait without tripping the catch. An average across all the birds can tell us only so much: within that, we have birds who saw more potential gain than risk in these populated places, and those whose calculations came out the other way around. We know that eagle owls, for instance, are generally willing to make urban forays in search of refuse-heap rodents or even nesting spots (quarries, housing blocks)—one lived for a short while in central Exeter in 2016, haunting the high-rise student digs, the football ground, the roof of the Odeon cinema. Conversely, we know that golden eagles, huge and unwieldy, uninterested in small fry like mice, not much given to scavenging, don't see the percentage in hanging around humans, and steer clear. We didn't find any golden eagle bones at Hallan Çemi. That might suggest that the bone-counts, in these cases, reflect natural patterns of bird behaviour, the birds' voluntary incursions into the town, and not just the fortunes of the bird-hunters home from the hills.

Let's zoom out, letting the neolithic townspeople recede in the viewfinder. Let's look again at the patterns of the birds. Astrophysicists, locked in their eternal battle with the limitations of human language, sometimes try to describe gravity by characterising space-time as a stretched rubber sheet, and objects with mass, like planets and stars, as weights placed on the sheet. As the sheet is distended, other objects placed on it will roll, as if attracted, towards the weights. For some bird populations, a town or a city works somewhat the same way: it's a pucker in the rubber sheet, a bulging node that creates new contour lines.

Populations don't move like individual birds, aren't drawn in like vultures are drawn to corpses, gulls to landfill, starlings to industrial hulks—the process is incremental, as messily concentric pockets of 'can' open in deserts of 'can't'. Where the city is, the pattern warps. We'll see something similar if we watch the large-scale drifts of birds over any rich habitat (a fertile mudflat, a saturated moss bog, an old-growth woodland), and we'll see the converse, by and large, over a desert or an icecap—but cities and towns are a bit different. They just *arrive*. They pop up more quickly than almost any other habitat. Desert edges creep outward, conifer plantations grow at bamboo speed, but nothing lands on a landscape as quickly or as heavily as towns do, as we do. *Boing*, goes the rubber sheet. And while for certain right-place, right-time species this new object does indeed seem to draw populations inward—starlings and rock doves roll right down the stretched rubber—for others, the effect is more as though something hefty has been shoved up from *underneath* the sheet. This is a disruptive geometry in the birds' space-time. Watch from above, from afar, and see the populations roll back—there's something repellent in the character of cities, too.

I wonder if we sometimes go too far when we talk about city birdlife. We can get overexcited, and lose a sense of proportion. Cities as a rule do not host a great variety of birds (typically just 8% or so of the species range found in the surrounding coun-tryside), and those that they do host are unlikely to vary much from city to city (for all that cities can be intense concentrations of human culture and thereby human difference, Sheffield, to a bird, looks much like Shanghai, Tapachula much like Trenton, NJ; Milton Keynes has its magpies much as Hallan Çemi did). These are no Edens.

In the decades since the Second World War we've changed the way we speak and think about urban birds, urban wildlife, edgeland ecology, the unofficial countryside. We have often been grudging and reluctant about it, but what was once an awkward accommodation made amid the fly haze of sewage farms, the electric hum of lines and pylons, the nodding buddleia jungles of city-centre brownfield is now something richer and deeper; we find it easier now to see sublimity and even romance in our urban wildlife—we're ready to see, now, how *charismatic* it can be.

We can blame Accipitridae, the raptors, the hawks, kites, eagles, for this. We're star-struck by our urban wildlife, and nothing has done so much to bring this on, to enliven and electrify our cities' roof-level ecospheres, as birds of prey. These are birds that must, in recent decades, have detected a shift somewhere in the infrastructure of these rocketing habitats of cliff and savanna, the throw of a few switches among thousands from 0 to 1 or 1 to 0, just enough to rejig the odds a little—just enough for the goshawks, the peregrines, the red kites to run the numbers and think, *yes, this can be done, we can be here.* Urban natural history has gone through a few poster-boys in its time (we might think of the blackening peppered moth, turning soot-grey as it forged a living in the smog days of the Industrial Revolution; we might think of the city fox and the black redstart, the car-park waxwing and the blue-tit on the milkbottle, the Tyne kittiwake and the London parakeet) but very few have had the A-list oomph of a peregrine stooping from a cathedral spire, a red kite banking low over the roof of a shopping centre, a goshawk tearing open a thrush on a path in a downtown park. These are the marquee names in city ecology today.

Really, it makes sense. City skies can be safe spaces for birds of prey. There are no gamekeepers in the Alexanderplatz, no shotguns on the Drottninggatan: city habitats tend to be free from the hostility that these species are liable to encounter over farmland and grouse-moor. Then there are the agglomerations of prey birds, the starlings and pigeons whose densities in modern cities often outstrip non-urban equivalents, and so draw in lanner falcon (over Addis Ababa, Harare, Nairobi, Accra), kārearea (over Rotorua), saker (over Vienna, Debrecen, Budapest ("a single observation… where a juvenile male followed a pigeon into a ventilating system")). Goshawks— historically city-sceptics, disdaining carrion, preferring the woodland-edge—feed on burgeoning woodpigeon and starling populations in Hamburg, Cologne and Berlin ("I hadn't quite pictured a goshawk sitting on a tower block", wrote Conor Jameson, struggling with cognitive dissonance in east Berlin in his 2013 book *Looking For The Goshawk*, "among television aerials and satellite dishes, disdaining the dive-bombing crows haranguing it"). Peregrines, too, are pretty new to our towns— the peregrine is distinctly a bird of the *modern* city, the "star skyline", the skyscraper city. But there are, where raptors are concerned, some overlaps between, say, mediaeval Mecklenburg or Roman Southwark and the Leeds, or Berlin, or Belgrade we know today.

Belgrade's Great War Island is now the hub of an urban white-tailed eagle population, which seems an extraordinary notion, like an urban wildebeest population or an urban ostrich population, yet another twenty-first century urban raptor "wow" moment, but in fact archaeologists have found the bones of the white-tailed eagle (12lb, 3ft x 9ft, the size of a pool table, the weight of a howitzer shell) in the Roman and mediaeval subsoil of towns across northern Europe: Oslo, Leicester, Oldenburg, Mecklenburg, Valkenburg, Chojnice, Bergen, Droitwich, Krepsk. Archaeologists have found that the white-tailed eagle was a fairly common scavenger in Roman and mediaeval towns; the bird's longstanding exile on the stony Norwegian coast was a result of its exclusion from pretty much every other part of western Europe, rather than any preference on the eagles' part. It's a common theme for raptors, this, the simple avian ecology of 'can' and 'can't' tweaked by human agency (guns, traps, poisons) into something more like 'may' and 'may not'. The white-tailed eagles were there, on Austvågøy, on Stormolla, because we wouldn't let them be anywhere else. But left to their own devices they're 'broad-spectrum feeders' —they'll eat any old shit—and their 'can' is a big place. When we loosen the screws the eagles' world expands like gas in a vacuum. Why *wouldn't* they be cruising dumps and bullying herring gulls for fish processors' discards? It's the smart move, just like battening on mediaeval towns (perhaps rootling in the middens or snatching sprats from unattended creels) was the smart move.

The kite, too, as we've seen, is finding a way in to the modern city as it found a way in to the old (two different habitats, but both offering profit for a bird with the kite's skillset). There's still something unavoidably jarring in the sight of a red kite, *Milvus milvus*, over the grey built-up edges of north-east Leeds, but look at its close cousin, the black kite, *Milvus migrans*, as it scraps for offal in Delhi, gathers in huge monsoon roosts in Kolkata, wheels over Hong Kong and the Pearl River megalopolis—it would seem mad to crunch this sprawling urban population into what's left of what we call countryside, to even think of it as a bird gone wrong or strayed for forsaking unpeopled places and moving to the city, as if the black kite were a doomed waif in a Theodore Dreiser novel. The birds regret nothing! If they can live there they'll live there.

The evolutions of cities send ripples through populations of kites and white-tailed eagles and other scavenging birds. Young cities—like young humans—make a lot of mess, of which faeces are often the most obtrusive; mature cities, sleeker and more polished, make just as much mess (more, in fact) but have generally learned to sluice it away, pipe it underground, stash it in undesirable districts, tow it by barge to far-off places, or have it otherwise disposed of. Those young years are the boom years for the scavengers: around the world, vultures—like the griffon vulture, *Gyps fulvus*, whose old bones wound up at Hallan Çemi—thrive as new cities germinate and grow, but then stutter as the cities develop sewerage and waste-management infrastructure. The pattern has been repeated hundreds of times over (in mediaeval London, it's reputed that legal statutes protected the red kite from persecution, such was its value as a street-cleaner). The upshot is that through the course of human history birds like the kite have been 'city birds' and then not 'city birds' and are now 'city birds' again, each time because what we mean by the word city has changed. It's not within the scope of this book to wonder how we'll come to think of the red kite in twenty or thirty years' time, if it continues to thrive and colonise in our cities—if it acquires a patina of urban grime, if it becomes a bin-bird (a "shite-hawk", as *Milvus migrans* was once known by British servicemen in the subcontinent); as it's seen knocking around with magpies and crows, scapegoats and hate-figures as they are—but I do wonder, anyway.

Kites and vultures prosper in what ecologists call a *donor-controlled* ecosystem. The idea is that, by growing accustomed to feeding on our generously strewn filth and food-waste, they become unmoored from the expected dynamics of predator-prey systems. This is one way looking at it. I think there are other ways.

Birds that feed in cities have to negotiate the traps we set: the cars and buses we drive, the power lines we string up from block to block, the diseases and toxins with which we spike our refuse, the foxes we feed (without meaning to, but that makes no odds), the panes of bewildering glass we put everywhere (twenty-five per cent of all US bird species have been documented flying into windows at one time or another). This is no pleasure cruise. It's not easy; if it were, everyone would be doing it. Where birds perish in our cities, that's predation. Never mind about motive or intent. Cities in this context are extensions of us. They're our funnelwebs, our pitfalls, our pitcherplant traps—and, by the same token, our waste is us, too: it has to be hunted out, tangled with, consumed and safely processed (sometimes it fights back, a scrapheap herring gull succumbs to avian botulism, a marabou stork chokes on wire or plastic)—again, no easy task, not a thing that any old bird can do. This is a predator-prey relationship. It just doesn't look like one.

The idea that ecological mechanisms can be put on hold just because we've got involved is a persistent one—understandably, as we don't, in our day-to-day lives, tend to feel as though we're in the same game as the birds and animals and insects around us. But the fact that we're not commonly hunted by wolfpacks or picked off by cheetahs doesn't put us 'outside' predator-prey relationships, any more than our hospitals and medicines put us 'outside' natural selection. These things can't be second-guessed or outwitted. They just happen; they're just happening. Sometimes (for most of us, right now, most of the time) the intensity is dialled down, but it's the same system, just running on different numbers.

When something as dazzling as a kite or a goshawk comes cruising into our city airspace, we can forgivably lose our sense of perspective. *This* is the story here, we think (we adopt the sensibility of a newspaper editor suffering a circulation dip— a sort of a *get me Superman!* syndrome).

Urban wildlife success stories can be thrilling. Events at the other end of the spectrum can make striking splash headlines, too: where we endanger a species, and where our role is clear-cut—as at Lodge Hill in Kent, where developers' housing blueprints call for the concreting-over of England's most important nightingale breeding grounds, or where shale-gas wells threaten to cripple pink-footed goose habitat on the

Ribble estuary—we respond, many of us, viscerally, powerfully, of course we do. But there's a danger in simplification (there's always a danger in simplification).

Bird life isn't a binary proposition, reducible in every case to *there* or *not there*. It's true—horrifyingly true—that habitat destruction, climate change and biodiversity decline at present constitute a three-carriage runaway train, that the pace of today's downhill plummet is hair-raising and unprecedented, but it's still the case that, by and large, bird populations don't vanish in a finger-snap. Bird life is still mostly attrititional; it's a question of erosion, resilience, reshaping. To put it another way, species decline isn't something that comes by stealth, it's not the bailiffs jemmying the door while the tenant's down the Jobcentre, it's not the bulldozers waiting till everyone's at work or the England game is on before they bring down the community woodland. It's something that is lived through; it's an accumulation of lived experience.

This is true even when we don't notice it. The birds have to live through it. There's nothing very newsy about a chaffinch's life getting slightly harder, a sparrow's prospects of sex or food getting incrementally worse, but these are the small sums that constitute a broader decline. This is how species die: day by day, being a bird gets just that little bit more difficult.

Helen Macdonald has written that "the rarer they get, the fewer meanings animals can have. Eventually rarity is all that they are made of." They end up stripped back to those binary statements, existence or extinction, and the life of birds as *they* know it goes unregarded. Except, of course, by evolution, the great grindstone: the small stuff, the dulled edge against the fractional advantage (what cycling coaches call *marginal gains*), these add up—and so the cliff swallows of North America's concrete highway bridges evolve slightly shorter wings, the better to manoeuvre out of the path of an oncoming eighteen-wheeler, and urban blackbirds—which may be on the brink of breakout speciation—evolve shorter bills and shriller voices, breed earlier, and sing for longer, amid the perpetual noise and light of the city.

It's less interesting to talk about gradations of hardship, the day-to-day cranking-up of difficulty in the lives of wild things, than it is to fill magazines with shots of skyscrapers and peregrines, or to show heartbreaking slides of shot hen harriers on grouse moors. We humans don't deal well with gradual change. We can see this as the world grows hotter and starts to seethe, and nothing is done, because wasn't today much the same as yesterday, and won't tomorrow be much the same as today? And we can see it because there were a thousand sparrows yesterday, and today there were nine hundred and ninety-nine, so what's the difference, what does it matter, who's counting? We don't feel the half-inch turn of the clamp. The change is barely there; the signal is a soft bleep lost in the noise. We don't feel the world tightening, hardening, getting harder to live in.

5. *Things to Come*

When I told people that I was writing this book and what it was about, the general consensus was that, in a history of birds and people, people were likely to emerge as very much the villains of the piece. After re-reading the book of Job, Virginia Woolf remarked: *I don't think God comes through well out of it.* You could say something similar, when you look at what humans have done, in every era of our time on this planet, on every continent, to the lives of birds—we don't come through well out of it.

I don't think birds spend much time worrying about people. And people, most of us, most of the time, for most of our history, haven't spent much time worrying about birds. We still don't—most of us, most of the time. Like the birds, we have other things to worry about. Being alive is a monumental undertaking.

A pair of blue tits with a clutch of chicks to feed might have to catch as many as a thousand caterpillars every day. This statistic makes me feel very stressed every time I read it; it explains why blue tits look so terribly knackered—faded, threadbare, dog-eared—at the end of the breeding season. A pair nests behind a grille on a wall opposite our house. It's not just caterpillars they have to worry about. I remember the year one of the local magpies found a way into their nest. And there are cats and crows and traffic and the odd sparrowhawk too. There's territory to maintain and harsh weather to see out (as I write this it's early May, and the female will be laying eggs; it's 5°C and tipping down).

I, meanwhile, am in far less mortal peril (touch wood) but I have things to worry about too—a mortgage to pay, a book to finish writing, a baby daughter to keep happy and safe, jobs to do around the house, relationships to maintain, paperwork to deal with, all the usual stuff, and that's before I start worrying about climate change, and Brexit, and Trump's America, and measles outbreaks, and the Tories, and the far-right, and Syria, and, and, and...

We all have a lot on. That's all. Most people have more to worry about than I do, some have less, we all have *something*—we're all pushed and pulled and prodded from a dozen different directions at once. Sometimes we screw up. Sometimes not screwing up is just too difficult (more difficult, very often, than it looks from the outside). This is worth remembering, I think, when we, as a species, seem cruel, or clumsy, thoughtless, selfish, destructive, stupid, blind—we have such a lot to care about, and very often we do a bad job of it.

I said at the start that no human has ever lived in a birdless world. I doubt that any human ever will—a world that's no good for birds will be no good for us, either. It's true that in the future birds will probably be thinner on the ground, further-flung, harder to see and hear, more often than not just over the next hill, across the border, a little way deeper into the forest. And it'll almost certainly be our fault that they are.

In May 2019, a landmark UN report—really more "mile-high warning sign" than "landmark"—assessed the state of decline across the natural world and the existential threat posed to humanity by this ongoing global-scale ecocide. Relative to amphibians, to coniferous trees, to reef-forming corals, birds are doing okay; relative to how they were a century ago, they're in deep trouble, as forest cover thins and vanishes, wetlands run dry, coastlines swim in fertiliser runoff and disposable plastics seep into the food chain.

My baby daughter, who wasn't born when I began writing this book (she arrived at the end of the first draft), will grow up in a new world. Warmer, busier, more connected, less green. The birds she sees and hears won't be the birds I saw and heard when I was five, ten, twenty, thirty. I don't know how they'll change but I know they'll change.

Perhaps—fingers crossed!—we'll make it all work. Perhaps our arrangement, the accommodation the birds have made with us, moving over, yielding ground, cohabiting where they could, will persist, in some renewed form, some tweaked, adaptive shape. Perhaps, thanks to some mighty (and fast-acting) effort of socio-industrial will, global temperatures will level off; it will be warmer—it already *is* warmer, warmer today than yesterday—and we may see bee-eaters spread across the European northwest as the climate grows more summery, we may see the normal range of the bug-loving hoopoe, mad pink crest, *poo-poo-poo* song and all, extend to the south of England, we may see, from satellites, the white caps of our uplands contract a little, see fewer snow buntings loitering around ski-resort picnics, see numbers of ptarmigan and dotterel drop in the census data, but that fragile global mean would go up only a degree and a half or so—we can make that work (we can overcome dry fields, shrinking wetland, water shortage, more frequent extreme weather events) if we try. Perhaps we'll begin to use less, make less and waste less—perhaps the birds will prove happy to trade their rations of bycatch and leftover for a little more room to nest, breed and live. The balance of birds, the internal proportions of the whole, may shift, as we throttle back on growth, and specialists, birds of narrow niches, the Bengal florican and the monkey-eating eagle, the kakapo and the corncrake, find ways to hang on, get by, scrape through (these are the small traders, the family greengrocers, the indie bookshops, of the avian economy; starlings are Google, pigeons are Amazon). Perhaps we'll make it all work.

Perhaps the world will continue to burn. There'll still be birds, as the climate is pushed beyond its elastic limit, and we scramble to respond (too late, too late)—the roasted tropics will empty of birdsong, landscapes will shift a rung up the ladder (wetland to grassland, scrub to desert, tundra to steppe, desert to *more* desert), ecologies will lurch out of place as prey species move (as oceanic surface temperatures rise, as the atlases of plantlife are redrawn) and predators move after them, and other predators move after *them*. The birds have been through climate change before but never in human history have the birds seen anything like this. As they pitch and roll in the turbulence they'll watch the whorls of human populations spread across the earth like soft clay under a steam-press, moving not so much *toward* anywhere as *away*: from drought, conflict, crop failures, urban breakdown. Their shadows will flicker over patchworked complexes of involuntary parks. Some birds will feel the tug of opportunity. Others—many more—will watch the numbers spin, will watch the odds, and watch them tumble.

Perhaps we'll continue being us, only more so. A tighter squeeze on the land we use. A heavier tread wherever we stand. Perhaps some hail-mary tech solution will stave off the climate crisis and the lesson will be that yes, we can *still* do whatever we like: we can't make a problem we can't solve. So perhaps we'll go on raising cities from swamps and turning every foot of land we find to our own purpose (that purpose simply to *keep going*, outward, upward, doing more, being more). We'll close up all the gaps, caulk them tight, make the world seamlessly human, give everything only one meaning, *our* meaning—we'll pull down shutters against the birds, not on purpose exactly but just because, well, they're not what we're for, birds aren't the point of us, and when we do that we'll lock out, too, those other dimensions, other readings, other meanings (that turn an office-block into a sea cliff or a city into a savannah or a border between countries into nothing at all, like a toddler turns a cardboard box into a spaceship).

All the birds now alive, every goldfinch on a teazelhead, every magpie on a gutter, every flickering summer swift (these are the birds I can see from my office window as I write), will die—of course they will, most within a year or two, some within a decade, all within, I hope, my lifetime, and we'll all die too, after a while, along with everything else. This isn't news to us (perhaps it would be news to the birds, or perhaps not). But *how* birds die is important to us. The deaths of birds are what make the patterns of birds, patterns in both time and space: in time, the brakes-off one-way plunge through evolution, like someone running off-balance, tilted perpetually on the brink of a faceplant but somehow keeping upright and still going forward, that saw *archaeopteryx* rattle through uncountable generations to become a goldcrest and a moa, an osprey and a dodo, a blackcap and an ostrich, each now at the front of a long queue of skeletons; in space, those images we have of the weather of birds, the prevailing climate of birds *here* or *there*, a population moving in like a stormfront, a species thinning out, a landmass emptying—the deaths of birds create these shapes (shapes to which the birds, in the main, are oblivious and indifferent). Our concerns about the birds, in short, aren't shared by the birds.

This book has been about seeing ourselves as the birds see us. To do that, I think, is to come to terms not only with how little we matter to them but also, as a kind of function of the birds' indifference, with how much they matter to us.

In some ways it's a nonsense to talk about "the birds' world" (*it's the birds' world*, as was once said of Sinatra—*we just live in it*). Our worlds, the little worlds of all living things, are enmeshed beyond all untangling. And yet we're not all one, the birds, us, the insects, worms, flowers, the rest, not exactly; we're walled up within our own experiences, our own capacities. We share a physical world but our sensory and mental worlds remain discrete, entire, complete. So we *can* talk about the birds' world, in this sense. It stands by itself, towering, broad and wonderful, spanning continents, scaffolded by its own needs, values and perceptions. We can bump up against it, and make it change shape; puncture it, and open up holes; back away, make room for it, and watch it grow. We can't really get *into* it.

Roll the focus a final time and draw back to see it all once again in panorama. Four hundred billion birds (give or take), turning and wavering in that multi-level murmuration, at once a heat map, an inkblot test, an evolving colony of spores or microbes, a clock's rigging of wheels and interlocking cogs—whatever it is, it's never still, never the same (they seem to repeat, to our dim senses, from our obscured view, each spring, each autumn, the swifts arriving (the globe still working), the storks departing, but the swifts and storks aren't the same, the world turning beneath them isn't the same, and *we're* not the same).

Faced with the idea of losing the birds, in whole or in part, a disinterested observer might turn to us, the humans, and shrug: *your loss*. They'd be right. That's exactly what it would be, in fact what it already is: our loss, as the world we know is stripped of richness, of depth, of chiming multiplicity—as birds vanish, and the meanings of things vanish with them. We might as well be burning books, shredding reels of film, taking sledgehammers to the cities of antiquity. Is this a petty human concern? Perhaps it is—but really, petty human concerns are the only sort we have.

To see across spans of time, beyond, even, the limits of our *own* time, into pre-history, to peer at the theropods through the gingko fronds, at toothy *archaeopteryx*, at the moa glancing up at the approach of footsteps, is a very human privilege. To see the patterns of the birds, these churning aggregations of lived experience, stretching across miles, across millennia, for what they are, ungraspable, protean, indomitable, magical—this is a privilege, too.

Bibliography

Prologue

On the first birds, ancient goshawks, penguins of prehistory, homecoming swifts, and the working of the globe.

A. Bramwell, *Ecology in the 20th Century: A History* (Yale, 1989)

K. K. Burnham, W. A. Burnham & I. Newton 'Gyrfalcon *Falco rusticolus* post-glacial colonization and extreme long-term use of nest sites in Greenland', *Ibis*, 151 (2009)

M. Cocker & R. Mabey, *Birds Britannica* (Chatto & Windus, 2005)

C. Finlayson, *Avian Survivors: The History and Biogeography of Palearctic Birds* (T. & A. D. Poyser, 2011)

R. M. Lockley, *Letters From Skokholm* (Little Toller, 2010)

R. Mabey, *The Common Ground: A Place for Nature in Britain's Future?* (Hutchinson, 1980)

M. P. Martyniuk, *Field Guide to Mesozoic Birds and Other Winged Dinosaurs* (Pan Aves, 2012)

W. J. Turner ed., *Nature in Britain* (Collins, 1946)

D. W. Yalden & U. Albarella, *The History of British Birds* (Oxford, 2009)

1. Messy Eaters

On messy eating, motorways, farming, the rock doves of Israel, arrow-storks, migrations, house sparrows of different kinds, and the meaning of us.

J. Cheshire & O. Uberti, *Where the Animals Go* (Particular Books, 2016)

E. W. Heymann & S. S. Hsia 'Unlike fellows: a review of primate–non-primate associations', *Biological Reviews*, 90 (2014)

B. Macdonald, 'Before The Farm' *BBC Wildlife*, July 2018

F. D. Meunier, C. Verheyden, P. Jouventin, 'Use of roadsides by diurnal raptors in agricultural landscapes', *Biological Conservation*, 92 (2000)

R. E. Moreau, 'The main vicissitudes of the European avifauna since the Pliocene', *Ibis*, vol.96 no.3 (1954)

A. Recchi & A. Gopher, 'Birds and humans in the Holocene: the case of Qumran Cave 24 (Dead Sea, Israel)', *Acta zoologica cracoviensia*, 45 (special issue) (2002)

G. P. Sætre, S. Riyahi, M. Aliabadian, J. S. Hermansen, S. Hogner, U. Olsson, M. F. Gonzalez Rojas, S. A. Sæther, C. N. Trier, & T. O. Elgvin, 'Single origin of human commensalism in the house sparrow', *Journal of Evolutionary Biology*, 25 (2012)

D. Serjeantson, *Manuals in Archaeology: Birds* (Cambridge, 2009)

M. A. Zeder, 'Domestication and early agriculture in the Mediterranean Basin: Origins, diffusion, and impact', *Proceedings of the National Academy of Sciences*, vol.105 no.33 (2008)

R. M. Zink, 'The evolution of avian migration', *Biological Journal of the Linnaean Society*, 104 (2011)

2. Accidental Conservationists

On the Māori and the moa, the human footprint, haile-shotte, Chernobyl, Mayak and the DMZ, epiphenomenal conservation, involuntary parks, and the power of wilderness.

D. R. Foster, G. Motzkin, D. Bernardos & J. Cardoza, 'Wildlife dynamics in the changing New England landscape', *Journal of Biogeography*, 29 (2003)

D. K. Grayson, 'The archaeological record of human impacts on animal populations', *Journal of World Prehistory*, vol.15 no.1 (2001)

B. Macdonald, *Rebirding: Rewilding Britain and its Birds* (Pelagic, 2019)

P. Milberg & T. Tyrberg, 'Naïve birds and noble savages: a review of man-caused prehistoric extinctions of island birds', *Ecography*, vol.16 no.3 (1993)

G. Monbiot, *Feral: Rewilding the Land, Sea and Human Life* (Penguin, 2014)

F. Pearce, 'Chernobyl 2016', *BBC Wildlife*, November 2016

F. Pearce, 'First visit to Russia's secret nuclear disaster site', *New Scientist*, 7 December 2016

T. Samojlik, I. D. Rotherham, B. Jędrzejewska, 'Quantifying historic human impacts on forest environments: A case study in Białowieża Forest, Poland', *Environmental History*, vol.18 no.3 (2013)

B. Sterling, 'The world is becoming uninsurable, part 3', viridiandesign.org/notes/1-25/Note%2000023.txt

E. Wagner, 'The DMZ's thriving resident: The crane', *Smithsonian Magazine*, April 2011

3. Movements

On dislocation, acclimatisation, de-extinction, Shakespeare's starlings, ducks vagrant and invasive, the kite, the heath hen, and death.

F. Bodsworth, *Last of the Curlews* (Longmans, 1955)

T. R. Dunlap, *Nature and the English Diaspora* (Cambridge, 1999)

N. Elkins, 'Further thoughts on the transatlantic vagrancy of landbirds to Britain & Ireland', *British Birds*, 101 (2008)

R. S. R. Fitter, *The Ark in our Midst* (Collins, 1959)

T. Gup, '100 Years of the Starling', *New York Times*, 1 September 1990

J. H. Gurney, *Early Annals of Ornithology* (Paul B. Minet, 1972)

R. Heisman, 'The sad story of Booming Ben, last of the heath hens', *JSTOR Daily*, 2 March 2016

H. Macdonald, *H is for Hawk* (Jonathan Cape, 2014)

F. Pearce, *The New Wild: Why Invasive Species will be Nature's Salvation* (Icon, 2015)

K. Thompson, *Where Do Camels Belong? The Story and Science of Invasive Species* (Profile, 2015)

4. Home

On different kinds of cliffs, termites, pigeons and black redstarts, the first towns, city raptors, human waste, donor-controlled ecosystems, urban glamour, and the tightening of the clamp.

J. Bevis, *Aaaaw to Zzzzzd: The Words of Birds: North America, Britain, and Northern Europe* (MIT Press, 2010)

P. Bircham, *A History of Ornithology* (Collins New Naturalist series, 2007)

J. F. Chace & J. J. Walsh, 'Urban effects on native avifauna: a review', *Landscape and Urban Planning*, 74 (2004)

M. Cocker, *Birds & People* (Jonathan Cape, 2013)

R. S. R. Fitter, *London's Natural History* (Collins New Naturalist, 1945)

D. G. Haskell, *The Songs Of Trees: Stories from Nature's Great Connectors* (Viking, 2017)

W. H. Hudson, *Birds In London* (1898; reissued Read Books, 2014)

R. K. Murton, *Man & Birds* (Collins New Naturalist, 1971)

S. Mulkeen & T. P. O'Connor, 'Raptors in towns: Towards an ecological model', *International Journal of Osteology*, 7 (1997)

E. M. Nicholson, *Birds & Men* (Collins New Naturalist series, 1951)

T. P. O'Connor, 'Human refuse as a major ecological factor in medieval urban vertebrate communities', *Human Ecodynamics. Symposia of the Association for Environmental Archaeology*, G. Bailey, R. Charles & N. Winder eds. (Oxbow Books, 2000)

E. Pollard & H. Strouts ed., *Wings over the Western Front: The First World War Diaries of Collingwood Ingram* (Day Books, 2014)

R. Stiles, B. Gasienica-Wawrytko, K. Hagen, H. Trimmel, W. Loibl, T. Totzer, M. Kostl, S. Pauleit, A. Schirmann & W. Feilmayr, 'Understanding the whole city as landscape: A multivariate approach to urban landscape morphology', *SPOOL*, vol.1 no.1 (2014)

M. F. de Vasconcelos, D. Hoffmann, M. C. de Araújo & P. Neves Vasconcelos, 'Bird-termite interactions in Brazil: A review with perspectives for future studies', *Biota Neotropica*, vol.15 no.1 (2015)

M. A. Zeder & M. D. Spitzer, 'New insights into broad-spectrum communities of the Early Holocene Near East: the birds of Hallan Çemi', *Quaternary Science Reviews*, 151 (2016)

5. Things to Come

On the future.

S. Díaz, J. Settele, E. S. Brondízio, H. T. Ngo, M. Guèze, J. Agard, A. Arneth, P. Balvanera, K. A. Brauman, S. H. M. Butchart, K. M. A. Chan, L. A. Garibaldi, K. Ichii, J. Liu, S. M. Subramanian, G. F. Midgley, P. Miloslavich, Z. Molnár, D. Obura, A. Pfaff, S. Polasky, A. Purvis, J. Razzaque, B. Reyers, R. Roy Chowdhury, Y. J. Shin, I. J. Visseren-Hamakers, K. J. Willis, and C. N. Zayas eds. 'IPBES: Summary for policymakers of the global assessment report on biodiversity and ecosystem services of the Intergovernmental Science-Policy Platform on Biodiversity and Ecosystem Services' (2019)

Acknowledgements

Thanks—for their help in bringing this little book into being:

To Colin Sackett at Uniformbooks; to John Bevis; to Mark Cocker, Tim Dee, David George Haskell, and Steve Rutt; to Professor Terry O'Connor; and to Jennie Condell and Pippa Crane.

To Professor Jim Smith at the University of Portsmouth; to Professor Dolly Jørgensen at the University of Stavanger; to Pete Short of the RSPB; and to all the staff at The Leeds Library, Leeds and Bradford Libraries, and the library service at the University of Leeds.

To my wife, Frin, and my daughter, Genevieve, with all my love.

Index